YORK NOTES

THE MERCHANT OF VENICE

WILLIAM SHAKESPEARE

WORKBOOK BY EMMA PAGE

The right of Emma Page to be identified as the Author of this Work
has been asserted by her in accordance with the Copyright,
Designs and Patents Act 1988

YORK PRESS
322 Old Brompton Road, London SW5 9JH

PEARSON EDUCATION LIMITED
Edinburgh Gate, Harlow,
Essex CM20 2JE, United Kingdom
Associated companies, branches and representatives throughout the world

First published 2018

10 9 8 7 6 5 4 3 2 1

ISBN 978–1–2922–3681–0

Illustrations by Sue Woollatt
Phototypeset by DTP Media
Printed in Slovakia

Photo credits: Kotomiti Okuma/Shutterstock for page 8 / zamzarina abdullah/Shutterstock for page 22 /
Andrey Burmakin/Shutterstock for page 29 top / monbibi/Shutterstock for page 31 top / KOKHAN YARYNA/
Shutterstock for page 33 / Astrid Gast/Shutterstock for page 43 / Oleksandr Rybitskiy/Shutterstock for
page 45 left / Thipwan/Shutterstock for page 45 right / Peter Hermes Furian/Shutterstock for page 48 /
Martyn Goddard/Alamy Stock Photo for page 51 / Alvov/Shutterstock for page 55

CONTENTS

PART FOUR:
THEMES, CONTEXTS AND SETTINGS

PART FIVE:
FORM, STRUCTURE AND LANGUAGE

PART SIX:
PROGRESS BOOSTER

PART ONE: Getting Started

Preparing for assessment

HOW WILL I BE ASSESSED ON MY WORK ON *THE MERCHANT OF VENICE*?

All exam boards are different but whichever course you are following, your work will be examined through at least three of these four Assessment Objectives:

Assessment Objectives	Wording	Worth thinking about ...
AO1	Read, understand and respond to texts. Students should be able to: • maintain a critical style and develop an informed personal response • use textual references, including quotations, to support and illustrate interpretations.	• How well do I know what happens, what people say, do, etc? • What do I think about the key ideas in the play? • How can I support my viewpoint in a really convincing way? • What are the best quotations to use and when should I use them?
AO2	Analyse the language, form and structure used by a writer to create meanings and effects, using relevant subject terminology where appropriate.	• What specific things does the writer 'do'? What choices has Shakespeare made? (Why this particular word, phrase or paragraph here? Why does this event happen at this point?) • What effects do these choices create? Suspense? Sympathy? Comedy?
AO3 *	Show understanding of the relationships between texts and the contexts in which they were written.	• What can I learn about society from the play? (What does it tell me about attitudes to race, religion and gender in Shakespeare's day, for example?) • What was society like in Shakespeare's time? Can I see it reflected in the text?
AO4 *	Use a range of vocabulary and sentence structures for clarity, purpose and effect, with accurate spelling and punctuation.	• How accurately and clearly do I write? • Are there small errors of grammar, spelling and punctuation I can get rid of?

* For *The Merchant of Venice*, AO3 is not examined by Eduqas; AO4 is not examined by Edexcel

Look out for the Assessment Objective labels throughout your York Notes Workbook – these will help to focus your study and revision!

The text used in this Workbook is the Oxford School Shakespeare edition, 2010.

How to use your York Notes Workbook

There are lots of ways your Workbook can support your study and revision of *The Merchant of Venice*. There is no 'right' way – choose the one that suits your learning style best.

1) Alongside the York Notes Study Guide and the text	2) As a 'stand-alone' revision programme	3) As a form of mock-exam
Do you have the York Notes Study Guide for *The Merchant of Venice*? The contents of your Workbook are designed to match the sections in the Study Guide, so with the play to hand you could: • read the relevant section(s) of the Study Guide and any part of the play referred to; • complete the tasks in the same section in your Workbook.	Think you know *The Merchant of Venice* well? Why not work through the Workbook systematically, either as you finish scenes, or as you study or revise certain aspects in class or at home. You could make a revision diary and allocate particular sections of the Workbook to a day or week.	Prefer to do all your revision in one go? You could put aside a day or two and work through the Workbook, page by page. Once you have finished, check all your answers in one go! This will be quite a challenge, but it may be the approach you prefer.

HOW WILL THE WORKBOOK HELP YOU TEST AND CHECK YOUR KNOWLEDGE AND SKILLS?

Parts Two to **Five** offer a range of tasks and activities:

These fun and quick-to-complete tasks check your basic knowledge of the text

These more open questions challenge you to show your understanding

This task focuses in on a key character, theme, technique, idea or relationship and helps you plan and write up paragraphs for an essay

A clear, quick way to visually record your progress

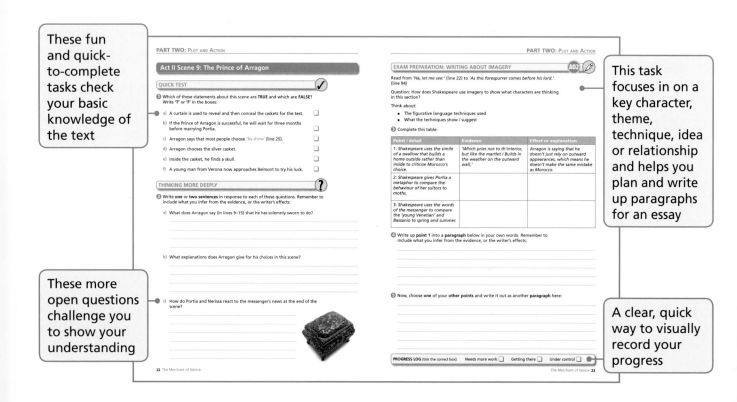

Each Part ends with a **Practice task** to extend your revision:

An exam-style task is provided at the end of each section for you to practise a full essay

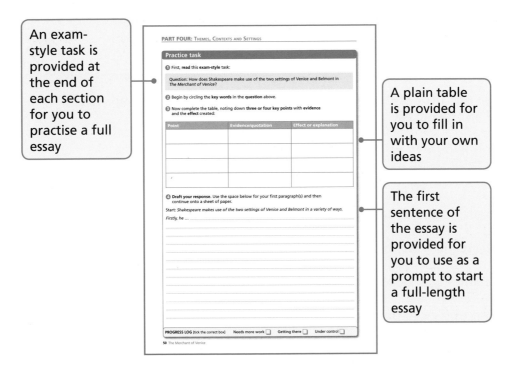

A plain table is provided for you to fill in with your own ideas

The first sentence of the essay is provided for you to use as a prompt to start a full-length essay

Part Six: Progress Booster helps you test your own key writing skills:

A sample of a student's writing challenges you to judge its strengths and weaknesses

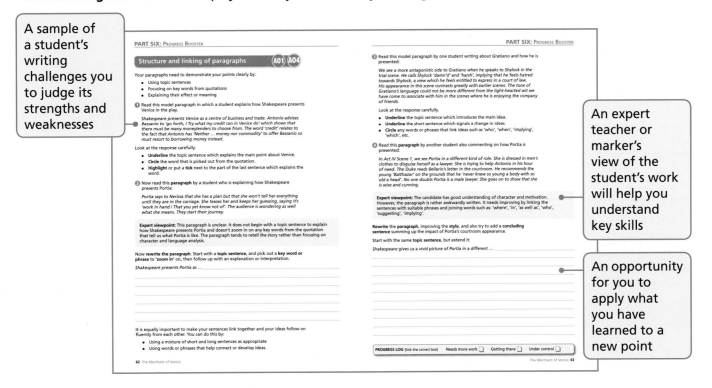

An expert teacher or marker's view of the student's work will help you understand key skills

An opportunity for you to apply what you have learned to a new point

Don't forget – these are just some examples of the Workbook contents. Inside there is much, much more to help you revise. For example:

- lots of samples of students' own work at different levels
- help with spelling, punctuation and grammar
- advice and tasks on writing about context
- a full answer key so you can check your answers
- a full-length practice exam task with guidance on what to focus on.

PART TWO: Plot and Action

Act I Scene 1: Bassanio's problem

QUICK TEST ✔

1 Which of these are **TRUE** statements about these scenes, and which are **FALSE**? Write **'T'** of **'F'** in the boxes:

a) Antonio is feeling sad at the beginning of the play. ☐

b) Gratiano and Lorenzo leave Antonio and Bassanio alone to talk. ☐

c) Antonio is suspicious of Bassanio's constant requests for money. ☐

d) Most of this scene is written in verse. ☐

e) Bassanio is already in debt. ☐

f) Bassanio can't propose to Portia because he is already married. ☐

g) Antonio has the money ready to lend to Bassanio. ☐

THINKING MORE DEEPLY ❓

2 Write **one** or **two sentences** in response to each of these questions. Remember to include what you infer from the evidence, or the writer's effects:

a) What first impressions would an audience get of Antonio?

....

....

....

....

b) What first impressions would an audience get of Bassanio?

....

....

....

....

....

c) What does Bassanio tell Antonio about Portia?

....

....

....

....

....

EXAM PREPARATION: WRITING ABOUT CHARACTERISATION

Read from: *'You look not well, Signor Antonio.'* (line 73) to *'… and when you have them they are not worth the search.'* (line 118)

Question: What picture of Gratiano does Shakespeare create?

Think about:

- The words used about Gratiano
- The words Gratiano uses

3 Complete this table:

Point / detail	Evidence	Effect or explanation
1: *Shakespeare presents Gratiano as concerned about his friend Antonio.*	*'You look not well, Signor Antonio.'* *'Believe me, you are marvellously chang'd.'*	*Gratiano's comments show he is sensitive to this dramatic change in his friend.*
2: *Gratiano suggests that some people stay quiet to seem wise but in actual fact they don't have anything interesting or wise to say.*		
3: *He is thought of as a funny character who talks a lot of nonsense.*		

4 Write up **point 1** into a **paragraph** below in your own words. Remember to include what you infer from the evidence, or the writer's effects:

....
....
....
....
....

5 Now, choose **one** of your **other points** and write it out as another **paragraph** here:

....
....
....
....
....
....

PROGRESS LOG [tick the correct box]   Needs more work ☐   Getting there ☐   Under control ☐

Act I Scene 2: Portia and her suitors

QUICK TEST ✔

1 **Tick** the box for the **correct answer** to each of these questions:

a) Which of Portia's suitors is described as only wanting to talk about his horse?

The County Palatine ☐   The Scottish lord ☐   The Neapolitan Prince ☐

b) Where does Falconbridge come from?

England ☐   Wales ☐   Ireland ☐

c) What is the name of Portia's French suitor?

Monsieur Le Tailleur ☐   Monsieur La Rue ☐   Monsieur Le Bon ☐

d) About which suitor does Portia say 'I fear he will prove the weeping philosopher when he grows old' (lines 46–7)?

The Scottish Lord ☐   The County Palatine ☐   The Prince of Morocco ☐

e) Who is on his way to Belmont to woo Portia and will arrive that night?

The Prince of Morocco ☐   The Duke of Saxony's nephew ☐
The Prince of Arragon ☐

THINKING MORE DEEPLY ?

2 Write **one** or **two sentences** in response to each of these questions. Remember to include what you infer from the evidence, or the writer's effects:

a) How is Portia feeling at the beginning of this scene?

....
....
....
....

b) What were Portia's father's instructions concerning the man she will marry?

....
....
....

c) What are the audience's impressions of the relationship between Portia and Nerissa, her lady-in-waiting?

....
....
....
....

EXAM PREPARATION: WRITING ABOUT VIEWPOINT A01

Read from: *'If I live to be as old as Sibylla …'* (line 98) to *'… another knocks at the door.'* (line 123)

Question: What does Portia say about her potential suitors in the final part of this scene?

Think about:

- What she says about the suitors who are about to go home
- What she says about the Prince of Morocco – and about a man she once met called Bassanio

3 Complete this table:

Point / detail	Evidence	Effect or explanation
1: *Portia is relieved that her suitors are leaving Belmont.*	*'there is not one among them but I dote on his very absence.'*	*The word 'dote' shows how much she longs for them to go. 'Dote' describes fond feelings towards a person, so the idea of doting on someone's absence is oxymoronic.*
2: *She does not wish to become Morocco's wife.*		
3: *She remembers Bassanio with enthusiasm.*		

4 Write up **point 1** into a **paragraph** below in your own words. Remember to include what you infer from the evidence, or the writer's effects:

....

....

....

....

....

5 Now, choose **one** of your **other points** and write it out as another **paragraph** here:

....

....

....

....

....

....

....

PROGRESS LOG [tick the correct box]   Needs more work ☐   Getting there ☐   Under control ☐

Act I Scene 3: A meeting with Shylock

QUICK TEST ✓

❶ **Number** the events of this scene so they are in the **correct sequence**. Use 1 for the first event and 7 for the final event.

a) Antonio enters and Shylock says, in an aside, that he hates Antonio and that Antonio hates all Jews. ☐

b) Shylock tells Bassanio that Antonio is a 'good' man, meaning he will be able to repay the loan. ☐

c) Antonio says he never lends or borrows with interest. ☐

d) Bassanio and Shylock discuss the loan, and that it is Antonio who 'shall be bound'. ☐

e) Shylock says that if Antonio does not repay the loan within three months, the 'forfeit' will be 'an equal pound / Of your fair flesh'. ☐

f) Shylock refuses Bassanio's invitation to dinner. ☐

g) Shylock says he has been the victim of ill treatment by Antonio. ☐

THINKING MORE DEEPLY ❓

❷ Write **one** or **two sentences** in response to each of these questions. Remember to include what you infer from the evidence, or the writer's effects:

a) Why is Shylock happy to lend to Bassanio?

....
....
....
....

b) How has Shylock been treated by Antonio in the past?

....
....
....

c) How does Bassanio's attitude to the arrangement with Shylock change during this scene?

....
....
....
....

EXAM PREPARATION: WRITING ABOUT LANGUAGE

Read from: *'How like a fawning publican he looks!'* (line 36) to *'Curs'd be my tribe / If I forgive him!'* (lines 46–7)

Question: In this aside, how does Shylock explain his attitude towards Antonio?

Think about:

- Shylock's criticisms of Antonio
- The language Shylock uses about Antonio

3 Complete this table:

Point / detail	Evidence	Effect or explanation
1: *Shylock criticises the way Antonio lends money without charging interest.*	*'He lends out money gratis, and brings down / The rate of usance here with us in Venice.'*	*The use of enjambment, emphasising the word 'down', shows Antonio's negative impact on the living Shylock and others can make as professional moneylenders.*
2: *He says that Antonio criticises Jews in general and him personally and professionally.*		
3: *He uses strong words to describe his intense feelings of dislike towards Antonio and his desire for revenge.*		

4 Write up **point 1** into a **paragraph** below in your own words. Remember to include what you infer from the evidence, or the writer's effects:

....

....

....

....

....

5 Now, choose **one** of your **other points** and write it out as another **paragraph** here:

....

....

....

....

....

....

PROGRESS LOG [tick the correct box]   Needs more work ☐   Getting there ☐   Under control ☐

Act II Scenes 1 and 2: Morocco arrives and Lancelot leaves

QUICK TEST ✓

1 Which of these statements about these scenes are **TRUE** and which are **FALSE**? Write 'T' or 'F' in the boxes:

a) The Prince of Morocco arrives dressed from head to toe in white clothing. ☐

b) Portia explains that her father restricted her choice of husband. ☐

c) Morocco refuses to swear that he will never propose to another lady. ☐

d) Lancelot Gobbo is loyal to his master. ☐

e) Lancelot speaks in prose. ☐

f) Lancelot complains that he has to do all the cooking. ☐

g) Old Gobbo mistakenly thinks Lancelot's hair is a long beard. ☐

THINKING MORE DEEPLY ?

2 Write **one** or **two sentences** in response to each of these questions about Act II Scene 2. Remember to include what you infer from the evidence, or the writer's effects:

a) How do we know that Lancelot Gobbo is debating whether to leave his master?

....

....

....

b) What do we learn about Old Gobbo in this scene?

....

....

....

c) Who offers Lancelot employment, and how does Lancelot respond to the offer?

....

....

....

....

....

EXAM PREPARATION: WRITING ABOUT COMIC EFFECTS

Read from *'Master young-man, you, I pray you ...'* (II.2.30) to *'I am a Jew if I serve the Jew any longer.'* (II.2.105)

Question: How does Shakespeare create comedy in this conversation between father and son?

Think about:

- The comedy of the situation
- The use of humorous language

❸ Complete this table:

Point / detail	Evidence	Effect or explanation
1: *Old Gobbo does not recognise his son.*	*'Do you not know me, father?'*	*Lancelot plays tricks on his father, taking advantage of his blindness and confusion.*
2: *Shakespeare creates opportunities for visual humour.*		
3: *The two men mispronounce various words and sayings.*		

❹ Write up **point 1** into a **paragraph** below in your own words. Remember to include what you infer from the evidence, or the writer's effects:

....

....

....

....

....

❺ Now, choose **one** of your **other points** and write it out as another **paragraph** here:

....

....

....

....

....

PROGRESS LOG [tick the correct box]   Needs more work ☐   Getting there ☐   Under control ☐

Act II Scenes 3 to 6: Jessica's escape

QUICK TEST

❶ Complete this **gap-fill paragraph** about the key events in these scenes:

Lancelot says goodbye to Shylock's daughter .... as he leaves to

work for .... She gives him a .... which he passes to

.... They secretly plan for Jessica to leave her home dressed in

.... clothing and taking with her some of Shylock's ....

and .... Even though he does not wish to attend the feast,

.... likes the idea of wasting Bassanio's .... He instructs

Jessica to stay at home but she elopes with Lorenzo, pretending to be his

.... as they prepare to enjoy the masque with their friends.

THINKING MORE DEEPLY ❓

❷ Write **one** or **two sentences** in response to each of these questions. Remember to include what you infer from the evidence, or the writer's effects:

a) How does Jessica feel about her father and her life with him?

....

....

....

....

b) What do we learn in these scenes about Lorenzo's thoughts and feelings towards Jessica?

....

....

....

....

c) How does Gratiano contribute to Act II, particularly Scene 6?

....

....

....

....

....

....

EXAM PREPARATION: WRITING ABOUT ATTITUDES

Read from *'I am bid forth to supper, Jessica.'* (II.5.11) to *'A proverb never stale in thrifty mind.'* (II.5.53)

Question: What do we learn about Shylock's attitudes to others in this scene?

Think about:

- The way Shylock speaks to the people around him
- The way Shylock speaks about characters in their absence

❸ Complete this table:

Point / detail	Evidence	Effect or explanation
1: *Shylock thinks Lancelot is lazy and greedy.*	*'Snail-slow in profit, and he sleeps by day / More than the wildcat. Drones hive not with me'*	*Shakespeare uses a series of animal images to convey Lancelot's laziness.*
2: *He takes a dim view of the partygoers.*		
3: *He wants both Bassanio and Antonio to suffer.*		

❹ Write up **point 1** into a **paragraph** below in your own words. Remember to include what you infer from the evidence, or the writer's effects:

....

....

....

....

....

❺ Now, choose **one** of your **other points** and write it out as another **paragraph** here:

....

....

....

....

....

....

PROGRESS LOG [tick the correct box]   Needs more work ☐   Getting there ☐   Under control ☐

Act II Scene 7: Morocco takes the test

QUICK TEST ✔

1 **Tick** the box for the **correct answer** to each of these questions:

a) What are three caskets made of?

Gold, silver and bronze ☐ Gold, silver and lead ☐ Gold, glass and wood ☐

b) How many times does the Prince of Morocco say the words 'gold', 'golden' or 'gilded' in this scene?

Three ☐ Five ☐ Nine ☐

c) Complete the inscription on the golden casket: 'Who chooseth me, shall gain

what many men ....' (line 5)

deserve ☐ desire ☐ choose ☐

d) What is inside the casket Morocco chooses?

A skull ☐ A portrait of a fool ☐ Portia's picture ☐

e) What else lies inside the casket?

Another puzzle to solve ☐ A rhyme written on a scroll ☐ A musical instrument ☐

THINKING MORE DEEPLY ?

2 Write **one** or **two sentences** in response to each of these questions. Remember to include what you infer from the evidence, or the writer's effects:

a) How does the Prince of Morocco praise Portia in this scene?

....

....

....

b) What reasons does he give for his choice of casket?

....

....

....

....

c) How does Morocco feel about his failure in the test? How does Portia feel?

....

....

....

....

....

EXAM PREPARATION: WRITING ABOUT LANGUAGE

Read from *'O hell! What have we here?'* (line 62) to *'thus losers part.'* (line 77)

Question: How does Shakespeare use language in the inscription on the casket?

Think about:

- Tone and style
- Rhythm and rhyme

3 Complete this table:

Point / detail	Evidence	Effect or explanation
1: *The inscription is written in short rhyming lines, with one end-rhyming sound throughout.*	*'Often have you heard that told. / Many a man his life hath sold / But my outside to behold.'*	*The short lines and use of rhyme create a playful tone, rather like a riddle.*
2: *The short poem addresses the failed suitor directly.*		
3: *Shakespeare creates some stark contrasts.*		

4 Write up **point 1** into a **paragraph** below in your own words. Remember to include what you infer from the evidence, or the writer's effects:

....

....

....

....

....

....

5 Now, choose **one** of your **other points** and write it out as another **paragraph** here:

....

....

....

....

....

....

....

PROGRESS LOG [tick the correct box]   Needs more work ☐   Getting there ☐   Under control ☐

Act II Scene 8: Bad news for Shylock and Antonio

QUICK TEST ✔

1 **Number** the events of this scene so they are in the **correct sequence**. Use 1 for the first event and 5 for the final event.

a) Salarino tells Solanio about a boat that ran into trouble in the English Channel. ☐

b) Solanio comments on how much love Antonio has for Bassanio. ☐

c) Solanio says that Salarino should tell Antonio this news but says he should not be told too suddenly. ☐

d) Salarino says that Antonio told Bassanio not to worry about the loan being repaid on time. ☐

e) Solanio reports that Shylock is mourning the disappearance of both his daughter and his money. ☐

THINKING MORE DEEPLY ?

2 Write **one** or **two sentences** in response to each of these questions. Remember to include what you infer from the evidence, or the writer's effects:

a) How would you describe Solanio and Salarino's role in this scene?

....

....

....

....

b) What kind of language do they use about Shylock in this scene?

....

....

....

....

c) How does this scene add to our impressions of Antonio?

....

....

....

....

....

EXAM PREPARATION: WRITING ABOUT CHARACTER

Read from *'I never heard a passion so confus'd'* (line 12) to *'Crying his stones, his daughter, and his ducats.'* (line 24)

Question: How is Shylock portrayed in Solanio and Salarino's account?

Think about:

- What Shylock is reported to have said
- Solanio and Salarino's language choices when speaking about Shylock

3 Complete this table:

Point / detail	Evidence	Effect or explanation
1: *Solanio and Salarino say Shylock was behaving strangely.*	*'a passion so confus'd, / So strange, outrageous, and so variable'*	*They use many adjectives to emphasise Shylock's confusion and repeat 'so' three times for effect.*
2: *The losses of Shylock's daughter and his money are presented as one and the same.*		
3: *Solanio and Salarino mock Shylock's reaction to his losses.*		

4 Write up **point 1** into a **paragraph** below in your own words. Remember to include what you infer from the evidence, or the writer's effects:

....

....

....

....

....

5 Now, choose **one** of your **other points** and write it out as another **paragraph** here:

....

....

....

....

....

....

PROGRESS LOG [tick the correct box]   Needs more work ☐   Getting there ☐   Under control ☐

Act II Scene 9: The Prince of Arragon

QUICK TEST ✓

1 Which of these statements about this scene are **TRUE** and which are **FALSE**?
Write **'T'** or **'F'** in the boxes:

a) A curtain is used to reveal and then conceal the caskets for the test. ☐

b) If the Prince of Arragon is successful, he will wait for three months
before marrying Portia. ☐

c) Arragon says that most people choose 'by show' (line 25). ☐

d) Arragon chooses the silver casket. ☐

e) Inside the casket, he finds a skull. ☐

f) A young man from Verona now approaches Belmont to try his luck. ☐

THINKING MORE DEEPLY ❓

2 Write **one** or **two sentences** in response to each of these questions. Remember to
include what you infer from the evidence, or the writer's effects:

a) What does Arragon say (in lines 9–15) that he has solemnly sworn to do?

....

....

....

....

b) What explanations does Arragon give for his choices in this scene?

....

....

....

....

c) How do Portia and Nerissa react to the messenger's news at the end of the
scene?

....

....

....

....

....

....

EXAM PREPARATION: WRITING ABOUT IMAGERY

Read from *'Ha, let me see:'* (line 22) to *'As this forespurrer comes before his lord.'* (line 94)

Question: How does Shakespeare use imagery to show what characters are thinking in this section?

Think about:

- The figurative language techniques used
- What the techniques show / suggest

❸ Complete this table:

Point / detail	Evidence	Effect or explanation
1: *Shakespeare uses the simile of a swallow that builds a home outside rather than inside to criticise Morocco's choice.*	*'Which pries not to th'interior, but like the martlet / Builds in the weather on the outward wall,'*	*Arragon is saying that he doesn't just rely on outward appearances, which means he doesn't make the same mistake as Morocco.*
2: *Shakespeare gives Portia a metaphor to compare the behaviour of her suitors to moths.*		
3: *Shakespeare uses the words of the messenger to compare the 'young Venetian' and Bassanio to spring and summer.*		

❹ Write up **point 1** into a **paragraph** below in your own words. Remember to include what you infer from the evidence, or the writer's effects:

....
....
....
....
....

❺ Now, choose **one** of your **other points** and write it out as another **paragraph** here:

....
....
....
....
....
....
....

PROGRESS LOG [tick the correct box]   Needs more work ☐   Getting there ☐   Under control ☐

Act III Scene 1: Trouble and despair

QUICK TEST ✔

❶ **Number** the events of this scene so they are in the **correct sequence**. Use 1 for the first event and 6 for the final event.

a) Shylock says that he wants revenge on Antonio due to how he has treated him because he is a Jew. ☐

b) Shylock speaks with Salarino and Solanio about his daughter's disappearance. ☐

c) Tubal confirms that Antonio has lost a ship and will be bankrupt. ☐

d) Shylock repeats that Antonio must 'look to his bond'. ☐

e) Salarino and Solanio say the rumours that Antonio has lost a ship continue. ☐

f) Tubal reports stories about Jessica spending Shylock's money in Genoa. ☐

THINKING MORE DEEPLY ?

❷ Write **one** or **two sentences** in response to each of these questions. Remember to include what you infer from the evidence, or the writer's effects:

a) What do we learn about Antonio's financial situation in this scene?

....
....
....
....

b) What exactly does Tubal tell Shylock about Jessica in Genoa?

....
....
....
....
....

c) What is the effect on Shylock of the news he hears in this scene?

....
....
....
....

EXAM PREPARATION: WRITING ABOUT SHYLOCK'S REVENGE (A01)

Read *'There I have another bad match'* (line 39) to *'… but I will better the instruction.'* (line 65)

Question: What does Shylock say about revenge in this extract?

Think about:

- What he says about revenge
- How he expresses his ideas

3 Complete this table:

Point / detail	Evidence	Effect or explanation
1: *Shylock suggests that Antonio is going to get what he deserves.*	*'Let him look to his bond. He was wont to call me usurer; let him look to his bond.'*	*Shylock repeats the phrase 'let him look to his bond' showing that he is determined to exact his revenge.*
2: *Shylock argues that taking revenge on someone who has wronged you is a natural human reaction.*		
3: *He suggests that in having his revenge, he will only be copying what Antonio has taught him.*		

4 Write up **point 1** into a **paragraph** below in your own words. Remember to include what you infer from the evidence, or the writer's effects:

....

....

....

....

....

5 Now, choose **one** of your **other points** and write it out as another **paragraph** here:

....

....

....

....

....

....

PROGRESS LOG [tick the correct box]   Needs more work ☐   Getting there ☐   Under control ☐

Act III Scene 2: Bassanio and the caskets

QUICK TEST ✓

❶ **Tick** the box for the **correct answer** to each of these questions:

a) Why does Portia suggest that Bassanio should not rush his decision?

She thinks he is not wealthy enough for her ☐   She does not want him to

choose the wrong casket ☐   She wants other suitors to do the test first ☐

b) Bassanio says 'For as I am, I live upon the rack' in line 25. What does he mean by the 'rack'?

An instrument of torture ☐   An island ☐   Something you gamble with ☐

c) What happens in the background while Bassanio chooses?

They feast ☐   Nerissa writes a letter ☐   Music plays ☐

d) Which casket does Bassanio choose?

Gold ☐   Silver ☐   Lead ☐

e) To whom does Nerissa become engaged?

Lorenzo ☐   Gratiano ☐   Leonardo ☐

THINKING MORE DEEPLY ?

❷ Write **one** or **two sentences** in response to each of these questions. Remember to include what you infer from the evidence, or the writer's effects:

a) What news does Salerio bring from Venice?

....

....

....

....

b) What effect does this news have on Bassanio?

....

....

....

....

c) What is Portia's response to the news?

....

....

....

....

EXAM PREPARATION: WRITING ABOUT ATMOSPHERE

Read from *'Madam, you have bereft me of all words.'* (line 175) to *'That ever blotted paper.'* (line 250)

Question: How does the mood change dramatically in this scene?

Think about:

- How the mood changes
- How Shakespeare achieves this

3 Complete this table:

Point / detail	Evidence	Effect or explanation
1: *The mood is at first romantic and celebratory.*	*'Good joy, my lord and lady!'* *'Our feast shall be much honour'd in your marriage.'*	*Portia and Bassanio are congratulated by Nerissa and Gratiano. News of a wedding is a plot device Shakespeare uses to end many comedies happily.*
2: *The letter changes Bassanio's mood and he speaks to Portia honestly about Antonio and the bond.*		
3: *Portia lifts the mood with her practical help and support.*		

4 Write up **point 1** into a **paragraph** below in your own words. Remember to include what you infer from the evidence, or the writer's effects:

....

....

....

....

....

5 Now, choose **one** of your **other points** and write it out as another **paragraph** here:

....

....

....

....

....

....

....

PROGRESS LOG [tick the correct box]   Needs more work ☐   Getting there ☐   Under control ☐

Act III Scenes 3, 4 and 5: Antonio's arrest and Portia's plan

QUICK TEST ✓

1 **Number** the events of these scenes so they are in the **correct sequence**. Use 1 for the first event and 7 for the final event.

a) Antonio says he accepts that the Duke of Venice will not 'deny the course of law'. ☐

b) Portia says she and Nerissa will go to stay in a monastery. ☐

c) Antonio says Shylock hates him because he helped people who had built up debts with Shylock. ☐

d) Lancelot teases Jessica and Lorenzo, and Jessica speaks in praise of Portia. ☐

e) Portia begins to explain her plan to Nerissa. ☐

f) Antonio has been arrested and Shylock threatens him with revenge. ☐

g) Portia asks Balthazar to take a letter to her cousin Doctor Bellario in Padua, and to return with the 'notes and garments' he gives him. ☐

THINKING MORE DEEPLY ?

2 Write **one** or **two sentences** in response to each of these questions. Remember to include what you infer from the evidence, or the writer's effects:

a) How would you describe Shylock's tone towards Antonio and the jailer in Scene 3?

....

....

....

....

b) In Scene 4, what reasons does Portia give for supporting Antonio?

....

....

....

....

c) What do we learn about Portia's plan to help Antonio in these scenes?

....

....

....

....

EXAM PREPARATION: WRITING ABOUT COMEDY

Read from *'Shall they see us?'* (III.4.59) to *'Defy the matter.'* (III.5.61)

Question: How does Shakespeare use humour in these scenes?

Think about:

- The characters and the language they use
- How Shakespeare balances comedy with dramatic tension

3 Complete this table:

Point / detail	Evidence	Effect or explanation
1: *Portia teases Nerissa about her plan.*	*'they shall think we are accomplished / With that we lack.'*	*Shakespeare uses humour to show that Portia has a quick-witted and rebellious side to her character.*
2: *Lancelot Gobbo – now employed by Bassanio – fondly teases Jessica.*		
3: *Lorenzo pokes fun at Lancelot and his choice of words.*		

4 Write up **point 1** into a **paragraph** below in your own words. Remember to include what you infer from the evidence, or the writer's effects:

....

....

....

....

....

....

5 Now, choose **one** of your **other points** and write it out as another **paragraph** here:

....

....

....

....

....

....

....

PROGRESS LOG [tick the correct box]   Needs more work ☐   Getting there ☐   Under control ☐

Act IV Scene 1: The trial

QUICK TEST ✔

❶ Which of these statements about this scene are **TRUE** and which are **FALSE**?
Write **'T'** or **'F'** in the boxes:

a) The Duke calls Antonio a 'stony adversary'. ☐

b) The court officers are known as 'Magnificoes'. ☐

c) Nerissa is dressed as a lawyer called Balthazar. ☐

d) Portia's speech in this scene is famous for the line 'O love, be moderate'. ☐

e) Shylock allows a surgeon to be present to prevent Antonio from
bleeding to death. ☐

f) Gratiano says that Shylock should be hanged. ☐

g) As a sign of his gratitude, Bassanio sends his ring to the lawyer (Portia). ☐

THINKING MORE DEEPLY ?

❷ Write **one** or **two sentences** in response to each of these questions. Remember to
include what you infer from the evidence, or the writer's effects:

a) What is the Duke of Venice's role in the trial?

....

....

....

....

b) What skills does Portia demonstrate during the trial?

....

....

....

....

....

c) Why do you think Portia asks Bassanio for his ring?

....

....

....

....

....

EXAM PREPARATION: WRITING ABOUT TENSION

Read from *'My deeds upon my head!'* (line 204) to *'A sentence: come, prepare.'* (line 302)

Question: How does Shakespeare create tension in this section?

Think about:

- Key moments in the scene's structure
- The language used

❸ Complete this table:

Point / detail	Evidence	Effect or explanation
1: Characters on both sides trade insults with each other.	'this currish Jew' 'Would any of the stock of Barrabas / Had been her husband, rather than a Christian!'	Shakespeare creates a confrontation where there is hatred and distrust between the two sides in this dispute.
2: Tension mounts when Portia says the bond is lawful.		
3: Shakespeare raises the tension even further when Shylock prepares to take his 'pound of flesh'.		

❹ Write up **point 1** into a **paragraph** below in your own words. Remember to include what you infer from the evidence, or the writer's effects:

....

....

....

....

....

❺ Now, choose **one** of your **other points** and write it out as another **paragraph** here:

....

....

....

....

....

....

PROGRESS LOG [tick the correct box]　　Needs more work ☐　　Getting there ☐　　Under control ☐

Act IV Scene 2 and Act V Scene 1: The rings and resolution

QUICK TEST

1 Complete this **gap-fill paragraph** about the key events in these scenes:

With the help of ...., Portia and Nerissa (still in disguise) arrange for

Shylock to sign the deed passing his wealth to .... They plan to leave

Venice and reach .... a day before their husbands. Gratiano brings

with him Bassanio's .... and Nerissa says in an aside that she will see

if she can get Gratiano to make the same gesture as Bassanio. Back in Belmont,

Lorenzo and Jessica speak in the .... and listen to ....

Portia and Nerissa return, followed by ...., Bassanio and Gratiano.

The husbands struggle to explain why they gave away their rings to ....

and his .... Eventually Portia explains everything and the happy

ending is complete when Nerissa gives Lorenzo the deed, and Antonio says that his

.... have returned safely.

THINKING MORE DEEPLY **?**

2 Write **one** or **two sentences** in response to each of these questions. Remember to include what you infer from the evidence, or the writer's effects:

a) What issue about married life is raised by the ring test and Lorenzo and Jessica's conversation?

....

....

....

....

b) Do you agree with the idea that the play ends happily? Why / why not?

....

....

....

....

c) Why do you think Shakespeare chooses not to end the play once the trial is over?

....

....

....

....

EXAM PREPARATION: WRITING ABOUT THE ENDING

Read from *'Speak not so grossly'* (V.1.266) to the end of the play.

Question: To what extent does Shakespeare bring the play to a satisfying conclusion in Act V?

Think about:

- The fortunes of the play's main characters
- The mood at the end of the play

❸ Complete this table:

Point / detail	Evidence	Effect or explanation
1: *When Nerissa gives Lorenzo Shylock's deed, Shakespeare resolves the future of Lorenzo and Jessica.*	*'My clerk hath some good comforts too for you.'*	*The word 'comforts' brings warm reassurance to Lorenzo and Jessica who were facing an uncertain future.*
2: *We hear that Antonio's ships are safe.*		
3: *Shylock does not appear in the final two scenes and is barely mentioned.*		

❹ Write up **point 1** into a **paragraph** below in your own words. Remember to include what you infer from the evidence, or the writer's effects:

....

....

....

....

....

❺ Now, choose **one** of your **other points** and write it out as another **paragraph** here:

....

....

....

....

....

....

PROGRESS LOG [tick the correct box]   Needs more work ☐   Getting there ☐   Under control ☐

Practice task

1 First, **read** this **exam-style** task:

In this scene, Antonio has been arrested and Shylock insists repeatedly that he will have his bond.

Read from: *'I'll have my bond'* (III.3.4) to *'and then I care not.'* (III.3.36)

Question: How does Shakespeare present Shylock and Antonio, and their feelings about their conflict, in this extract and in the play as a whole?

2 Begin by circling the **key words** in the **question** above.

3 Now complete the table, noting down **three or four key points** with **evidence** and the **effect** created:

Point	Evidence/quotation	Effect or explanation

4 **Draft your response**. Use the space below for your first paragraph(s) and then continue onto a sheet of paper.

Start: *In this extract, Shakespeare presents Shylock as someone who has become obsessed with revenge. At the beginning of this extract, he …* ....

....

....

....

....

....

....

....

....

....

....

PROGRESS LOG [tick the correct box]   Needs more work ☐   Getting there ☐   Under control ☐

PART THREE: CHARACTERS

Who's who?

1 Look at these drawings and add the missing information for each character.

a) Name: Antonio

Who: _Merchant_ _of_ _Venice_

b) Name: _Portia_

Who: wealthy heiress

c) Name: Bassanio

Who: _man who wants_ _to woe portia_

d) Name: _Shylock_

Who: Jewish moneylender, Jessica's father

e) Name: Nerissa

Who: _Portia's_ _made_

f) Name: Gratiano

Who: _Bassanio's_ _friend_

g) Name: _Lorenzo_

Who: friend of Bassanio and Gratiano, marries Jessica

h) Name: Lancelot Gobbo

Who: _Shylock's_ _old servant_

i) Name: Jessica

Who: _Shylock's_ _daughter_

2 Which characters from the play are missing above? Fill in the table below.

Royalty / nobles	Venetian citizens	Venetian Jews	Servants, messengers, etc.
Judge		Pubal	Solnano Salerio

Antonio

1. Without looking at the play, **write down from memory** two pieces of information we are told about Antonio in each of these areas:

Antonio's business dealings as a merchant	1: .... 2: ....
Antonio's attitude towards Shylock	1: He doesn't like him, ... 2: ....
Antonio's friendship with Bassanio	1: .... 2: ....

Now **check your ideas**. Are you right? Look at the following scenes from the play:

- Antonio's business dealings as a merchant: Act I Scene 1, Act III Scene 2, Act V Scene 1
- Antonio's attitude towards Shylock: Act I Scene 3, Act III Scene 1, Act IV Scene 1
- Antonio's friendship with Bassanio: Act I Scene 1, Act II Scene 8, Act IV Scene 1

2. **Complete** these **quotations** either by Antonio about himself, or by other characters describing him:

a) Antonio: 'In sooth I know now why I am so ....'

b) Gratiano: 'You have too much .... upon the world:'

c) Salarino: 'A .... gentleman treads not the earth.'

d) Shylock: 'Jailer, look to him. Tell not me of mercy. /

   This is the .... that lent out money gratis.'

e) Antonio: 'I am a .... wether of the flock'

PROGRESS LOG [tick the correct box]   Needs more work ☐   Getting there ☐   Under control ☐

Portia

1 Look at these statements about Portia and decide whether they are **True [T]**, **False [F]** or whether there is **Not Enough Evidence [NEE]**.

a) Portia doesn't want to be married at all. [T] [F] [NEE]

b) Portia respects her father's wishes. [T] [F] [NEE]

c) Portia and Nerissa are good friends. [T] [F] [NEE]

d) Portia is disappointed that Bassanio passes the casket test. [T] [F] [NEE]

e) Portia wants to help Antonio because he is Bassanio's friend. [T] [F] [NEE]

f) Portia knew about the safe return of some of Antonio's ships all along. [T] [F] [NEE]

2 **Complete** these **statements** about Portia:

a) *Portia shows a cruel side to her character when* …

b) *When Bassanio is successful in the casket test, Portia reacts by* …

c) *Portia's performance as a lawyer in the trial scene is* …

d) *We learn that Portia enjoys having power over other characters in the play, when* …

and when …

PROGRESS LOG [tick the correct box]   Needs more work ☐   Getting there ☐   Under control ☐

Shylock

1 Complete this **gap-fill paragraph** about Shylock with the correct information:

Shylock is a Jewish usurer or .... living in Venice. In Act I Scene 3, he

agrees to the loan of three thousand .... as an act of friendship, saying he

will forget ....'s harsh treatment of him in the past. However, the bond

they agree allows Shylock to claim a pound of the merchant's .... if the

money is not repaid within .... months. In Act II, Shylock's ....

Jessica runs away with Lorenzo, taking many of her father's .... with

her. In Act IV Scene 1, ...'s legal skills deprive Shylock of his revenge.

Ultimately Shylock is not treated mercifully by the .... establishment. In

the final two scenes, Shylock does not .... at all.

2 Using your **own judgement**, draw a line on this graph to show your response to **Shakespeare's presentation** of Shylock at different points in the play.

Very sympathetic

Quite sympathetic

A little sympathetic

Totally unsympathetic

Act I   Act II   Act III   Act IV

3 Now record **evidence** to support each point on your graph in the table below:

Act	Evidence
I	
II	
III	
IV	

PROGRESS LOG [tick the correct box]   Needs more work ☐   Getting there ☐   Under control ☐

Bassanio

1 Tick the name of the character who makes these statements about, or to, Bassanio.

a) 'I am half yourself / And I must freely have the half of anything / That this same paper brings you.' (III.2.246–8)

Antonio ☐   Portia ☐   Lancelot ☐

b) 'I'll go in hate to feed upon / The prodigal Christian' (II.5.14–15)

Shylock ☐   Old Gobbo ☐   Jessica ☐

c) 'Bassanio, Lord Love, if thy will it be!' (II.9.100)

Portia ☐   Nerissa ☐   Messenger ☐

d) 'I speak too long, but 'tis to peize the time, / To eche it, and to draw it out in length, / To stay you from election.' (III.2.22–4)

Gratiano ☐   Antonio ☐   Portia ☐

2 Write **one or two sentences** in response to these questions:

a) Why does Bassanio ask Antonio for money in Act I Scene 1?

....

....

....

b) How does Bassanio feel about Antonio borrowing the money from Shylock?

....

....

....

c) How honest / dishonest is Bassanio with Portia? Provide evidence.

....

....

....

3 Using your **own judgement**, put a mark along this line to show **Shakespeare's overall presentation** of Bassanio.

Not at all sympathetic	A little sympathetic	Quite sympathetic	Very sympathetic
❶	❷	❸	❹

PROGRESS LOG [tick the correct box]   Needs more work ☐   Getting there ☐   Under control ☐

Other characters

1 **Who says** each of the following? **Tick** the correct character.

a) 'Gave it a judge's clerk! No, God's my judge

The clerk will ne'er wear hair on's face that had it.' (V.1.157–8)

Duke of Venice ☐   Jessica ☐   Nerissa ☐

b) 'I was always plain with you, and so now I speak my agitation of the matter.' (III.5.3–4)

Prince of Arragon ☐   Lancelot Gobbo ☐   Tubal ☐

c) 'Upon my power I may dismiss this court,' (IV.1.104)

Shylock ☐   Duke of Venice ☐   Nerissa ☐

d) 'My eyes, my lord, can look as swift as yours:

You saw the mistress, I beheld the maid.' (III.2.197–8)

Gratiano ☐   Lorenzo ☐   Lancelot Gobbo ☐

2 Write **two sentences** explaining the significance of these characters to the play as a whole:

a) *I think Lancelot Gobbo is significant to the play as a whole because ...* ....

....

....

....

b) *I think Lorenzo is significant to the play as a whole because ...* ....

....

....

....

c) *I think Salarino and Solanio are significant to the play as a whole*

because ... .

....

....

....

....

....

3 **Fill in following table** with details of the inscriptions on and contents of each casket.

	Gold casket	Silver casket	Lead casket
Inscription			
Contents			
Who chose it?			

4 Write below what each suitor's choice of casket suggests about his character.

The Prince of Morocco:
The Prince of Arragon:
Bassanio:

5 Look at the bank of **adjectives** below. Choose an adjective that you think could be used to describe each of the following characters. Then find a piece of evidence to support your choice of adjective.

supportive	loyal	decisive	cruel	dignified
clever	strong	foolish	comical	rash

Character	Adjective	Evidence
Nerissa		
Duke of Venice		
Gratiano		
Prince of Arragon		

PROGRESS LOG [tick the correct box] Needs more work ☐ Getting there ☐ Under control ☐

Practice task

1 First, **read** this **exam-style** task:

Question: How does Shakespeare present Portia as both witty and wise in the play as a whole?

2 Begin by circling the **key words** in the **question** above.

3 Now complete the table, noting down **three or four key points** with **evidence** and the **effect** created:

Point	Evidence/quotation	Effect or explanation

4 **Draft your response**. Use the space below for your first paragraph(s) and then continue onto a sheet of paper.

Start: *From her first appearance in Act I Scene 2, Shakespeare presents Portia as a quick-witted character …* ....

....

....

....

....

....

....

....

....

....

....

PROGRESS LOG [tick the correct box]   Needs more work ☐   Getting there ☐   Under control ☐

PART FOUR: THEMES, CONTEXTS AND SETTINGS

Themes

1 **Circle** the **themes** you think are most relevant to *The Merchant of Venice*:

ambition   (mercy)   (love)   violence   risk   guilt

(revenge)   chance   (family)   (the law)   (money)   beauty

(appearance versus reality)   (greed)   (prejudice)   evil   loyalty

(justice and injustice)   (marriage)   conflict   fate   (power)

2 **Who says**? Each of these quotations relates to a theme, but which one (or more), and who is speaking?

a) 'so is the will of a living daughter curbed by the will of a dead father'

Theme(s): *Family , power*   Speaker: *Portia*

b) 'Gilded tombs do worms infold.'

Theme(s): ....   Speaker: ....

c) 'I'll plague him, I'll torture him.'

Theme(s): *Revenge*   Speaker: *Shylock*

d) 'We do pray for mercy, / And that same prayer doth teach us all to render / The deeds of mercy.'

Theme(s): *Mercy*   Speaker: *Portia*

e) 'I am a Jew. Hath not a Jew eyes?'

Theme(s): *Prejudice*   Speaker: *Shylock*

f) 'I shall never see my gold again. Four score ducats at a sitting!'

Theme(s): *Money , greed*   Speaker: *Shylock*

THINKING MORE DEEPLY

3 Think about the themes of **money**, **trade** and **commerce**.

a) In what ways is money important in the storyline involving Antonio, Shylock and the bond? List four key ways.

Antonio's life depends on money for if he can't pay, a pound of flesh will be taken. It is important as Shylock wants money but it changes its importance when he can take revenge

b) In what ways is money important in the storylines involving Portia? Write **one or two sentences**:

Bassanio needs money to woe Portia his love, he uses it to decieve her so he can marry her. She also uses her money to try and save Antonio from Shylock.

4 **Tests and trials** are important in the play. Can you think of **three occasions** when characters undergo a trial or test? Which of the play's themes are significant in each of these examples?

Test 1: Bassanio choosing between the caskets

Themes: Love, Chance

Test 2: Shylock choosing between money and revenge

Themes: greed, law, revenge, hatred

Test 3: Rings

Themes: Power, Love

5 **Friendship** is an important theme in the play. Write **two to three sentences** on the friendships between these characters:

Portia and Nerissa: They show the female love and friendship. They have a laugh but it shows that Portia has more power and influence

Antonio, Bassanio and Portia:

6 In the play, some characters treat others with **prejudice** and discriminate on the grounds of race or religion. Fill in the table below with examples of **language** that:

- reveal prejudiced attitudes (column 1)
- describe being the victim of such attitudes (column 2).

The first ones have been done for you.

Reveal prejudiced attitudes	Describe being the victim of such attitudes
Gratiano: 'infidel'	Shylock: 'You call me misbeliever, cut-throat dog, / And spit upon my Jewish gaberdine.'

7 Think about the themes of mercy and revenge.

a) List the ways that characters show each other **mercy** in the play.

....

....

....

b) List the ways that characters are **vengeful** towards each other in the play.

....

....

....

c) In your opinion, which is the **most powerful force** in the play: mercy or revenge? **Explain** how you reached that conclusion.

....

....

....

....

....

EXAM PREPARATION: WRITING ABOUT LOVE AND MARRIAGE

Read from *'A gentle scroll!'* (III.2.139) to *'Our feast shall be much honour'd in your marriage.'* (III.2.212)

Question: Starting with this extract, explore how Shakespeare presents love and marriage in *The Merchant of Venice*.

Think about Shakespeare's presentation of love and marriage in this extract and the rest of the play.

8 Complete this table:

Point / detail	Evidence	Effect or explanation
1: Shakespeare presents the union of Bassanio and Portia as a moment of sheer joy and elation.	'Giddy in spirit' (Bassanio) 'Happiest of all' (Portia) 'you have bereft me of all words' (Bassanio)	Adjectives like 'giddy' and 'happiest' show that true affection has a deep impact on characters.
2: Shakespeare reveals a different side to marriage through the other suitors Portia encounters.		
3: Shakespeare uses this scene to show the harmony that marriage brings as Gratiano and Nerissa announce their love too.		

9 Write up **point 1** into a **paragraph** below in your own words. Remember to include what you infer from the evidence, or the writer's effects:

....

....

....

....

....

10 Now, choose **one** of your **other points** and write it out as another **paragraph** here:

....

....

....

....

....

....

PROGRESS LOG [tick the correct box]   Needs more work ☐   Getting there ☐   Under control ☐

Contexts

1 **Choose** the **correct answer** to these questions:

a) In which decade did Shakespeare write *The Merchant of Venice*?

1580s ☐   1590s ☐   1600s ☐

b) Which Italian text contains a story that inspired Shakespeare's play?

Il Pecorone ☐   *Il Postino* ☐   *La Dolce Vita* ☐

c) Which of Shakespeare's fellow Elizabethan playwrights wrote *The Jew of Malta?*

Ben Jonson ☐   Christopher Marlowe ☐   John Webster ☐

d) What is the name of the traditional Venetian boat that is mentioned in the play?

canoe ☐   lagoon ☐   gondola ☐

e) Although there were very few Jews in England at the time the play was written, Rodrigo Lopez was one famous exception. Who was he?

The Queen's doctor ☐   The Queen's tailor ☐   The Queen's treasurer ☐

f) Despite his early success at court, Lopez was accused of treason. What happened to him?

He was banished ☐   He was pardoned ☐   He was executed ☐

g) What does the word 'gentile' mean?

Atheist ☐   Non-Jewish ☐   Of the ghetto ☐

h) What word means the transfer of parental wealth and property to the husband when a daughter marries?

Duty ☐   Dowry ☐   Ducats ☐

2 Write **one or two sentences** in answer to each of these questions:

a) When Shakespeare wrote the play, anti-Semitic views were widely held. How is this shown in the play?

....

....

....

....

....

....

b) Money-lending (or usury) was a profession associated with Jews in Elizabethan times. Where is 'interest' (or 'usance') mentioned in the play?

....

....

....

....

....

c) At the time Shakespeare wrote the play, Venice was a major trading centre. How does Shakespeare remind us of this in the play?

....

....

....

....

....

3 Label these four places on the map and describe their importance in the play:

Venice	*Genoa*	*Naples*	*Padua*

a) ....

....

....

....

b) ....

....

....

....

c) ....

....

....

....

d) ....

....

....

....

PROGRESS LOG [tick the correct box]   Needs more work ☐   Getting there ☐   Under control ☐

Settings

1 Fill in the table below about the play's two main settings.

Questions	Venice	Belmont
Is it a real place or a fictitious place?		
Which scenes take place there? Circle the correct scenes.	I.1 I.2 I.3 II.1 II.2 II.3 II.4 II.5 II.6 II.7 II. 8 II.9 III.1 III.2 III.3 III.4 III.5 IV.1 IV.2 V.1	I.1 I.2 I.3 II.1 II.2 II.3 II.4 II.5 II.6 II.7 II.8 II.9 III.1 III.2 III.3 III.4 III.5 IV.1 IV.2 V.1
Which characters live there?		
Which key events take place there?		

2 Give three pieces of information about the settings in these scenes:

a) **Act III Scene 5** takes place in ....

Who it involves ....

Why the setting is important ....

....

....

b) **Act IV Scene 1** takes place in ....

Who it involves ....

Why the setting is important ....

....

....

c) **Act IV Scene 2** takes place in ....

Who it involves ....

Why the setting is important ....

....

PROGRESS LOG [tick the correct box]   Needs more work ☐   Getting there ☐   Under control ☐

Practice task

❶ First, **read** this **exam-style** task:

Question: How does Shakespeare make use of the two settings of Venice and Belmont in *The Merchant of Venice*?

❷ Begin by circling the **key words** in the **question** above.

❸ Now complete the table, noting down **three or four key points** with **evidence** and the **effect** created:

Point	Evidence/quotation	Effect or explanation

❹ **Draft your response.** Use the space below for your first paragraph(s) and then continue onto a sheet of paper.

Start: *Shakespeare makes use of the two settings of Venice and Belmont in a variety of ways.*

Firstly, he … ....

....

....

....

....

....

....

....

....

....

....

....

....

PROGRESS LOG [tick the correct box]   Needs more work ☐   Getting there ☐   Under control ☐

PART FIVE: FORM, STRUCTURE AND LANGUAGE

Form

1 How many Acts is the play divided into?

Five ☐   Three ☐   Four ☐

2 Which of the following best describes the genre of *The Merchant of Venice*?

Comedy ☐   History play ☐   Tragedy ☐

3 Which of these forms cannot be found within *The Merchant of Venice*?

Songs ☐   Letters ☐   A play within a play ☐

4 Draw lines to link these stage directions to the relevant Act and Scene:

Enter Portia *disguised as* Doctor Balthazar, *followed by officials*	*Act II Scene 9*
Arragon *unlocks the silver casket*	*Act V Scene 1*
Enter Lancelot Gobbo, *the Clown, alone*	*Act II Scene 6*
Enter Jessica *above, in boy's clothes*	*Act IV Scene 2*
Venice: a street. Enter Portia *and* Nerissa	*Act IV Scene 1*
Enter Stephano *with musicians*	*Act II Scene 2*

5 **Find one example** of a comic episode in the play and write a paragraph explaining its effects.

....

....

....

....

....

....

....

....

....

....

....

PROGRESS LOG [tick the correct box]   Needs more work ☐   Getting there ☐   Under control ☐

Structure

QUICK TEST ✓

1 Which of these statements relating to the structure of the play are **TRUE** and which are **FALSE**? Write **'T'** or **'F'** in the boxes:

a) The whole play takes place in Venice. ☐

b) There are three scenes in which caskets are chosen and opened. ☐

a) Jessica leaves her father's household in Act II. ☐

b) Shylock only appears in Acts I, II and III. ☐

2 Match the opening lines of these speeches to the Act and Scene in which they feature and the character who says them.

'The quality of mercy is not strain'd'   Bassanio, Act III Scene 2

'So may the outward shows be least themselves'   Gratiano, Act I Scene 1

'Let me play the Fool.'   Portia, Act IV, Scene 1

THINKING MORE DEEPLY ?

3 Draw a line on this graph to show moments of **high and low tension** in the play.

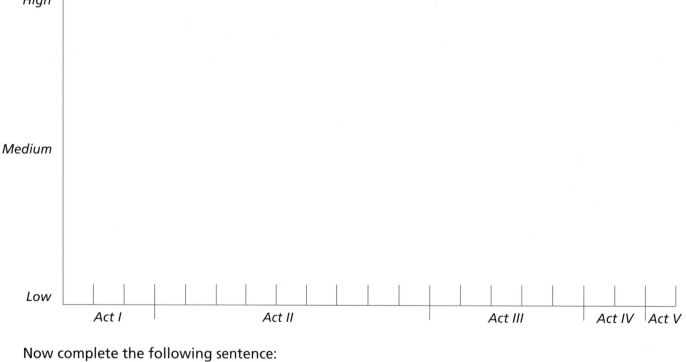

Now complete the following sentence:

I think that tension is at its highest point in the play in Act .... *Scene* .... *because* ... .

....

....

....

EXAM PREPARATION: WRITING ABOUT STRUCTURE

Question: How does Shakespeare use structural elements such as foreshadowing and moments of comedy in *The Merchant of Venice*?

Think about:

- Examples of structural elements
- The effect they have on the mood of the play

4 Complete this table:

Point / detail	Evidence	Effect or explanation
1: *Shakespeare uses the bond that is agreed to in Act I to foreshadow later events.*	*'I like not fair terms and a villain's mind.'*	*Bassanio casts Shylock in the role of 'villain', setting up the dark conflict at the heart of the play.*
2: *Shakespeare moves the action to Belmont in Act II, and Portia's witty commentary on her suitors.*		
3: *When the action moves back to Venice, Lancelot Gobbo makes a typically comical appearance to defuse tension.*		

5 Write up **point 1** into a **paragraph** below in your own words. Remember to include what you infer from the evidence, or the writer's effects:

....

....

....

....

....

....

6 Now, choose **one** of your **other points** and write it out as another **paragraph** here:

....

....

....

....

....

PROGRESS LOG [tick the correct box]   Needs more work ☐   Getting there ☐   Under control ☐

Language

1 Tick the box for the **correct word** to complete these examples of **imagery** from the play:

a) Solanio: 'Nature hath fram'd strange fellows in her time:

Some that will evermore peep through their eyes,

And laugh like .... at a bagpiper'

parrots ☐   peacocks ☐   piglets ☐

b) Shylock: 'The patch is kind enough, but a huge feeder,

.... –slow in profit, and he sleeps by day
More than the wildcat.'

Sloth ☐   Slug ☐   Snail ☐

c) Bassanio: 'Thus ornament is but the guiled shore

To a most dangerous ....'

sea ☐   tide ☐   wave ☐

d) Gratiano: 'for thy desires

Are ...., bloody, starv'd and ravenous.'

woeful ☐   wicked ☐   wolfish ☐

e) Lorenzo: 'When the sweet wind did gently .... the trees,

And they did make no noise.'

blow ☐   kiss ☐   stroke ☐

2 Choose one of the examples of **imagery** above and write a paragraph explaining its **effects** and linking it to a key **theme** of the play.

....

....

....

....

....

....

....

....

❸ The following **motifs** run through the play, but they may have many meanings. In each case you are given two scenes in which the motif appears. Explain the meanings or ideas connected to the motif in each scene.

a) **Flesh and / or blood** Act III Scene 1	
Act IV Scene 1	
b) **Ships and the sea** Act I Scene 1	
Act II Scene 8	
c) **Chance or risk** Act I Scene 1	
Act II Scene 7	

EXAM PREPARATION: WRITING ABOUT LANGUAGE

Question: How does Shakespeare use language to show characters' strong feelings?

Think about:

- The use of vocabulary and imagery
- How the intensity of feelings is conveyed

4 Complete this table:

Point / detail	Evidence	Effect or explanation
1: *Shylock is spoken about using anti-Semitic insults.*	'thou damn'd, inexecrable dog' 'Thou almost mak'st me waver in my faith, … That souls of animals infuse themselves / Into the trunks of men.'	Gratiano compares Shylock to animals. He is saying he is barely human and that he will not receive God's grace. This shows the intensity of his antipathy and prejudice.
2: *Shakespeare's characters also show their intense feelings of love and affection.*		
3: *Shylock seems to confuse his grief at the loss of his daughter with his grief at the loss of his money.*		

5 Write up **point 1** into a **paragraph** below in your own words. Remember to include what you infer from the evidence, or the writer's effects:

....

....

....

....

....

6 Now, choose **one** of your **other points** and write it out as another **paragraph** here:

....

....

....

....

....

PROGRESS LOG [tick the correct box]   Needs more work ☐   Getting there ☐   Under control ☐

Practice task

1 First, **read** this **exam-style** task:

Read from *'So may the outward shows be least themselves'* (III.2.73) to *'Joy be the consequence!'* (III.2.107).

Question: How does Shakespeare use language to convey the idea that outward appearances can be deceptive?

Think about:

- Shakespeare's use of language in this extract
- Shakespeare's use of language at other relevant points in the play

2 Begin by circling the **key words** in the **question** above.

3 Now complete the table, noting down **three or four key points** with **evidence** and the **effect** created:

Point	Evidence/quotation	Effect or explanation

4 **Draft your response**. Use the space below for your first paragraph(s) and then continue onto a sheet of paper.

Start: *In this extract, Shakespeare uses language to convey the idea that outward appearances can be deceptive. Firstly, he …*

PROGRESS LOG [tick the correct box]   Needs more work ☐   Getting there ☐   Under control ☐

PART SIX: Progress Booster

Writing skills

1 How well can you express your ideas about *The Merchant of Venice*? Look at this grid and tick the level you think you are currently at:

Level	How you respond	What your spelling, punctuation and grammar are like	Tick
Higher	• You analyse the effect of specific words and phrases very closely (i.e. 'zooming in' on them and exploring their meaning). • You select quotations very carefully and you embed them fluently in your sentences. • You are persuasive and convincing in the points you make, often coming up with original ideas.	• You use a wide range of specialist terms (words like 'imagery'), excellent punctuation, accurate spelling, grammar, etc.	
Mid	• You analyse some parts of the text closely, but not all the time. • You support what you say with evidence and quotations, but sometimes your writing could be more fluent to read. • You make relevant comments on the text.	• You use a good range of specialist terms, generally accurate punctuation, usually accurate spelling, grammar, etc.	
Lower	• You comment on some words and phrases but often you do not develop your ideas. • You sometimes use quotations to back up what you say but they are not always well chosen. • You mention the effect of certain words and phrases but these are not always relevant to the task.	• You do not have a very wide range of specialist terms, but you have reasonably accurate spelling, punctuation and grammar.	

SELECTING AND USING QUOTATIONS

2 Read these two samples from students' responses to a question about how Antonio is presented. Decide which of the three levels they fit best, i.e. **lower** (L), **mid** (M) or **higher** (H).

Student A: *Antonio says he is sad at the start of the play. His friends try to cheer him up but Antonio does not know why he is sad. He says 'I have much ado to know myself', suggesting that he does not usually feel like that.*

Level? ☐   Why? ....

....

Student B: *Shakespeare's presentation of Antonio's sadness opens the whole play. Comparing the world to a stage, Antonio says that 'every man must play a part, / And mine a sad one'. The final phrase 'And mine a sad one' implies that he is resigned to the idea that he must suffer this depression.*

Level? ☐   Why? ....

....

ZOOMING IN – YOUR TURN!

Here is the first part of another student response. The student has picked a good quotation but hasn't 'zoomed in' on any particular words or phrases:

When Antonio asks Bassanio about Portia, Bassanio starts to explain his money problems to his friend. The younger man says that 'my chief care / Is to come fairly off from the great debts' suggesting that he is looking for help.

❸ Pick out one of the **words** or **phrases** the student has quoted and write a further sentence to complete the explanation:

The word / phrase '...................................' suggests that..........................

....

....

EXPLAINING IDEAS

You need to be precise about the way Shakespeare puts ideas across. This can be done by varying your use of verbs (not just using 'says' or 'means').

❹ Read this paragraph from a **mid-level** response to a question about women in the play. Circle all the **verbs** that are repeated (not in the quotations):

In this scene Shakespeare conveys to the audience that Portia is quick-witted when she is talking with her friend and lady-in-waiting Nerissa. Portia says that she 'dote[s] on [their] very absence' when she is talking about her suitors. She is saying that she will be glad when they have left Belmont. It not only shows that she is becoming impatient with all her unsuitable suitors but it also shows she is independent.

❺ Now choose some of the words below to replace your circled ones:

suggests	implies	tells us	presents	signals	asks
demonstrates	recognises	comprehends	reveals	conveys	

❻ Rewrite your **higher-level** version of the paragraph in full below. Remember to mention the **author by name** to show you understand he is **making choices** in how he presents characters, themes and events.

....

....

....

....

....

....

....

PROGRESS LOG [tick the correct box]   Needs more work ☐   Getting there ☐   Under control ☐

Making inferences and interpretations

A02

WRITING ABOUT INFERENCES

You need to be able to show you can read between the lines, and make inferences, rather than just explain more explicit 'surface' meanings.

Here is an extract from one student's **very good** response to a question about Shylock and how he is presented:

In Act III Scene 1 Shylock is agitated about Jessica's disappearance as shown in his accusations 'You knew … of my daughter's flight' and his exclamations 'My own flesh and blood to rebel!' This tells us that he knows she has left him and believes that she has gone of her own free will as an act of rebellion. It also suggests that he is suspicious of Solanio, Salarino and their friends. He may feel that she has been lured away and so becomes increasingly interested in getting his revenge on Antonio, a respected figure in this group of friends – from which Shylock is an outcast.

1 Look at the response carefully.

- **Underline** the simple point which explains what Shylock does.
- **Circle** the sentence that develops the first point.
- **Highlight** the sentence that shows an inference and begins to explore wider interpretations.

INTERPRETING – YOUR TURN!

2 Read the opening to this student response carefully and then **choose the sentence** from the list which shows **inference** and could lead to **a deeper interpretation**. Remember – interpreting is *not* guesswork!

Nerissa asks her mistress to describe her feelings towards her suitors when she says 'But what warmth is there in your affection towards any of these princely suitors that are already come?' This shows that she is trying to help Portia with this difficult process. It also suggests that …

a) *… she is angry with Portia for being so moody given that Portia has so many eligible suitors who want to marry her.*

b) *… she is rudely invading Portia's privacy because as her lady-in-waiting she should not comment or offer advice.*

c) *… she is being ironic in her use of 'warmth', 'affection' and 'princely' because she agrees with Portia that these suitors are lacking in some way.*

3 Now **complete** this **paragraph** about Gratiano, adding your own final sentence which makes inferences or explores wider interpretations:

Gratiano is presented in the opening scene as comical and talkative. Bassanio jokes that Gratiano's ideas are 'as two grains of wheat hid in two bushels of chaff'.

This simile suggests that … ....

....

....

PROGRESS LOG [tick the correct box]   Needs more work ☐   Getting there ☐   Under control ☐

Writing about context

EXPLAINING CONTEXT

When you write about context you must make sure that what you write is relevant to the task.

Read this comment by a student about Lancelot Gobbo:

Lancelot Gobbo is described by Shakespeare in the stage directions as 'the Clown'. This shows us that this character would probably have been played in Shakespeare's time by the popular comic actor Will Kemp who also would have played clownish characters such as Peter in 'Romeo and Juliet'. The prose spoken by Lancelot is appropriate both for this character's social status and for the comic nature of this whole scene which creates humour from mistaken choices of words and mistaken identity.

1 Why is this an effective paragraph about context? Select a), b) or c).

   a) Because it says that Lancelot Gobbo is very funny.

   b) Because it makes the link between the character of Lancelot Gobbo and the stock character of the fool in Shakespeare's time.

   c) Because it explains everything I know about the fools in Shakespeare plays.

EXPLAINING – YOUR TURN!

2 Now read this further paragraph, and complete it by choosing a suitable point related to context, selecting from a), b) or c) below.

   Racial and religious prejudice is an important theme in the play and mirrors attitudes to Jews and Judaism at the time. Many of the Christian characters insult, criticise and mock Shylock. There is also evidence of racial prejudice in Portia's words, when she says …

   a) *'Let all of his complexion choose me so.'* This echoes Morocco's own use of the word 'complexion' in an earlier scene and suggests that judgements based on skin colour were commonplace at this time.

   b) *'If you choose that, then I am yours withal'.* This suggests that she is resigned to the outcome of the casket test.

   c) *'if you choose wrong, / Never to speak to lady afterward / In way of marriage'* which is a reminder to the audience of the solemn oath that all of her suitors must swear.

3 Now, on a separate sheet of paper, write a further paragraph about Portia's situation as a wealthy heiress in relation to the contexts of attitudes to women's status in society, marriage and inheritance in Shakespeare's time.

PROGRESS LOG [tick the correct box]   Needs more work ☐   Getting there ☐   Under control ☐

Structure and linking of paragraphs

Your paragraphs need to demonstrate your points clearly by:

- Using topic sentences
- Focusing on key words from quotations
- Explaining their effect or meaning

1 Read this model paragraph in which a student explains how Shakespeare presents Venice in the play.

Shakespeare presents Venice as a centre of business and trade. Antonio advises Bassanio to 'go forth, / Try what my credit can in Venice do' which shows that there must be many moneylenders to choose from. The word 'credit' relates to the fact that Antonio has 'Neither … money nor commodity' to offer Bassanio so must resort to borrowing money instead.

Look at the response carefully.

- **Underline** the topic sentence which explains the main point about Venice.
- **Circle** the word that is picked out from the quotation.
- **Highlight** or put a **tick** next to the part of the last sentence which explains the word.

2 Now read this **paragraph** by a student who is explaining how Shakespeare presents Portia:

Portia says to Nerissa that she has a plan but that she won't tell her everything until they are in the carriage. She teases her and keeps her guessing, saying it's 'work in hand / That you yet know not of'. The audience is wondering as well what she means. They start their journey.

Expert viewpoint: This paragraph is unclear. It does not begin with a topic sentence to explain how Shakespeare presents Portia and doesn't zoom in on any key words from the quotation that tell us what Portia is like. The paragraph tends to retell the story rather than focusing on character and language analysis.

Now **rewrite the paragraph**. Start with a **topic sentence**, and pick out a **key word or phrase** to 'zoom in' on, then follow up with an explanation or interpretation.

Shakespeare presents Portia as … ....

....

....

....

....

....

It is equally important to make your sentences link together and your ideas follow on fluently from each other. You can do this by:

- Using a mixture of short and long sentences as appropriate
- Using words or phrases that help connect or develop ideas.

❸ Read this model paragraph by one student writing about Gratiano and how he is presented:

We see a more antagonistic side to Gratiano when he speaks to Shylock in the trial scene. He calls Shylock 'damn'd' and 'harsh', implying that he feels hatred towards Shylock, a view which he feels entitled to express in a court of law. His appearance in this scene contrasts greatly with earlier scenes. The tone of Gratiano's language could not be more different from the light-hearted wit we have come to associate with him in the scenes where he is enjoying the company of friends.

Look at the response carefully.

- **Underline** the topic sentence which introduces the main idea.
- **Underline** the short sentence which signals a change in ideas.
- **Circle** any words or phrases that link ideas such as 'who', 'when', 'implying', 'which', etc.

❹ Read this **paragraph** by another student also commenting on how Portia is presented:

In Act IV Scene 1, we see Portia in a different kind of role. She is dressed in men's clothes to disguise herself as a lawyer. She is trying to help Antonio in his hour of need. The Duke reads Bellario's letter in the courtroom. He recommends the young 'Balthazar' on the grounds that he 'never knew so young a body with so old a head'. No one doubts Portia is a male lawyer. She goes on to show that she is wise and cunning.

Expert viewpoint: The candidate has good understanding of character and motivation. However, the paragraph is rather awkwardly written. It needs improving by linking the sentences with suitable phrases and joining words such as: 'where', 'in', 'as well as', 'who', 'suggesting', 'implying'.

Rewrite the **paragraph**, improving the **style**, and also try to add a **concluding sentence** summing up the impact of Portia's courtroom appearance.

Start with the same **topic sentence**, but extend it:

Shakespeare gives us a vivid picture of Portia in a different ... .

....

....

....

....

....

....

....

....

....

| PROGRESS LOG [tick the correct box] | Needs more work ☐ | Getting there ☐ | Under control ☐ |

Spelling, punctuation and grammar

Here are a number of key words you might use when writing in the exam:

Content and structure	Characters and style	Linguistic features
scene	character	simile
quotation	role	juxtaposition
sequence	comedy	dramatic irony
dialogue	protagonist	repetition
climax	dramatic	symbol
development	villainous	foreshadowing
description	humorous	malapropism
suspense	sympathetic	rhyme

1 Circle any you might find difficult to spell, and then use the 'Look, Say, Cover, Write, Check' method to learn them. This means: **look** at the word; **say** it out loud; then **cover** it up; **write** it out; uncover and **check** your spelling with the correct version.

2 Create a **mnemonic** for five of your difficult spellings. For example:

rhyme: **R**ight **H**ere **Y**our **M**usical **E**ffect!

Or break the word down into syllables:

SYM – PATH – ET – IC

a) ....

b) ....

c) ....

d) ....

e) ....

3 Circle any **incorrect spellings** in this paragraph and then rewrite it:

In the first scene, Shakespeare firmly establishes the freindship between two major caracters, Antonio and Bassanio. The audiense also learns about the weallthy Portia and the younger man's plans to woo her. Antonio agrees to help Bassanio who is gratefull to his patron. However, Antonio cannot raise the money without a lone, and so they agree to see a moneylender.

....

....

....

....

....

....

4 **Punctuation** can help make your meaning clear.

Here is one response by a student commenting on Shakespeare's exploration of the theme of money. Check for correct use of:

- Apostrophes
- Speech marks for quotations and emphasis
- Full stops, commas and capital letters

Shakespeare set's his play in Venice at the time this was a major centre of trade, the plays title makes many references to trade the professions of the 'merchant' of the title (antonio) and shylock are extremely important to the plot as when antonio says 'I'll seal to such a bond, he is agreeing to something that will put his life in danger

Rewrite it **correctly** here:

....

....

....

....

5 It is better to use the **present tense** to describe what is happening in the play.

Look at these two extracts. Which one uses tenses **consistently** and **accurately**?

Student A: *Shakespeare conveyed in Act II the difficulty of Jessica's situation. She appears desperate to leave her father's home and eventually she was able to elope with Lorenzo. She defied her father's wishes whereas Portia accepts the will of her father despite finding its strict conditions frustrating.*

Student B: *Shakespeare conveys in Act II the difficulty of Jessica's situation. She appears desperate to leave her father's home, eventually eloping with Lorenzo. Jessica defies her father's wishes whereas Portia accepts the will of her father despite finding its strict conditions frustrating.*

6 Now look at this further paragraph. **Underline** or **circle** all the **verbs** first.

In a comic soliloquy in Act II Scene 2, Lancelot Gobbo debated whether to leave 'this Jew, my master' or to stay. His language in this speech borrowed from the morality play tradition; his 'conscience' and a 'fiend' spoke to him in two different voices. Shakespeare gave Lancelot long words and long sentences and made him stumble over them: 'and, in my conscience, my conscience is but a kind of hard conscience'. The playwright contrasted the grand and ambitious style of the clown's language and the humorous effects it created for the audience to enjoy.

Now rewrite it using the **present tense** consistently:

....

....

....

....

....

PROGRESS LOG [tick the correct box]   Needs more work ☐   Getting there ☐   Under control ☐

Tackling exam tasks   (A01) (A02)

DECODING QUESTIONS

It is important to be able to identify **key words** in exam tasks and then quickly generate some ideas.

1 Read this task and notice how the **key words** have been underlined.

Question: *What is the <u>dramatic</u> and <u>thematic significance</u> of the <u>casket test</u> scenes?*

Write about:

- The <u>dramatic function</u> of these scenes
- How <u>Shakespeare</u> explores key <u>themes</u> in these scenes.

Now **underline** the **key words** in this task:

Question: *How does Shakespeare explore the different kinds of bonds that connect people in* The Merchant of Venice?

Write about:

- Ideas about relationships between family members and friends
- The techniques Shakespeare uses to explore these ideas

GENERATING IDEAS

2 Now you need to generate ideas quickly. Use the spider diagram* below and add as many ideas of your own as you can:

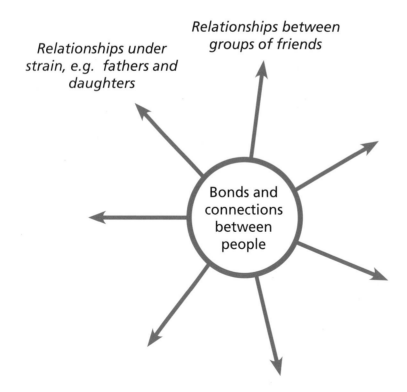

*You can do this as a list if you wish.

PLANNING AN ESSAY

Here is the **exam-style** task from the previous page:

Question: *How does Shakespeare explore the different kinds of bonds that connect people in* The Merchant of Venice?

Write about:

- Ideas about relationships between family members and friends.
- The techniques Shakespeare uses to explore these ideas

❸ **Using the ideas you generated** in the spider diagram or list in Question 2, write a simple **plan** with at least **five key points** (the first two have been done for you). Check back to the spider diagram or list you made.

a) *Relationships under strain, e.g. Portia's irritation at her father's dying wishes; Jessica's desertion from her family home*

b) *Relationships between groups of friends, e.g. the men who go to the masque*

c) ....

....

d) ....

....

e) ....

....

❹ Now list **five quotations** for each point (the first two have been provided for you):

a) *Jessica: 'But though I am a daughter to his blood / I am not to his manners.'*

b) *Bassanio: 'we have friends / That purpose merriment'*

c) ....

....

d) ....

....

e) ....

....

❺ Now read this task and **write a plan of your own**, including **quotations**, on a separate sheet of paper.

Read Act I Scene 3.

Question: *How is Shylock depicted in this scene and how do Antonio and Bassanio respond to him?*

PROGRESS LOG [tick the correct box]   Needs more work ☐   Getting there ☐   Under control ☐

Sample answers (A01) (A02) (A03) (A04)

OPENING PARAGRAPHS

Here is the task from the previous page:

Question: *How does Shakespeare explore the different kinds of bonds that connect people in* The Merchant of Venice?

Write about:

- Ideas about relationships between family members and friends.
- The techniques Shakespeare uses to explore these ideas

Now look at these two alternative openings to the essay and read the expert viewpoints underneath:

Student A

> *At the start of this play, Bassanio asks his friend for help to pay off his creditors. Antonio then takes out a loan on his behalf with a Jewish moneylender. Shakespeare is showing that the characters in the play are connected in different ways, and we see how these 'bonds' develop and are tested by circumstances as the play goes on.*

Student B

> *In the play, Antonio and Shylock agree to a 'bond' to secure Shylock's loan of three thousand ducats to Bassanio. The bond shows that a business agreement has been made and this means that Shylock wants to know all about Antonio and his ships because of the 'bond'.*

Expert viewpoint 1: This is a clear opening paragraph that suggests the kinds of 'bonds' that the answer will discuss in more depth. It also suggests that these 'bonds' connect people in different ways. However, the candidate should have said a little more at this stage about what those 'different ways' might be.

Expert viewpoint 2: This opening explains the bond that is agreed to by Antonio and Shylock, without outlining more generally what is to be discussed in the essay in response to the key word 'bonds', which is the point of the introduction. Other kinds of relationships need to be mentioned and explored.

❶ Which comment belongs to which answer? Match the paragraph (A or B) to the expert's feedback (1 or 2).

Student A: ....   **Student B:** ....

❷ Now it's your turn. Write the opening paragraph to this task on a separate sheet of paper:

Read Act II Scene 7.

Question: *What techniques does Shakespeare use to create comedy in this scene?*

Remember:

- Introduce the topic in general terms, perhaps **explaining** or **'unpicking'** the key **words** or **ideas** in the task (such as 'techniques' and 'comedy').
- Mention the **different possibilities** or ideas that you are going to address.
- Use the **author's name**.

WRITING ABOUT TECHNIQUES

Here are two paragraphs in response to a different task, where the students have focused on the writer's techniques. The task is:

Read from *'Is your name Shylock?'* (IV.1.174) to *'O excellent young man!'* (IV.1.244)

Question: *How is Portia depicted in this extract and how does Shylock respond to her? Refer closely to details from the extract to support your answer.*

Student A

> *Portia uses powerful language and convinces everyone that she really is the clever, young lawyer Balthazar that Doctor Bellario has sent to Venice in his place. She asks for mercy in a long persuasive speech. She says 'I have spoke thus much/To mitigate the justice of thy plea,/ Which if thou follow, this strict court of Venice/ Must needs give sentence 'gainst the merchant there.' However, Shylock still only wants his bond.*

Student B

> *Portia speaks confidently and extremely skilfully in her role as lawyer. She uses formal legal terms such as 'plea', 'precedent' and 'impugn' and asks direct questions of Shylock and Antonio in a legalistic cross-examining style ('You stand within his danger, do you not?'). She addresses the court at length about the importance of showing mercy. Crucially she gives Shylock, who says he 'craves the law', the impression that there is a good chance that his claim will be legally upheld, saying that 'there is no power in Venice/Can alter a decree established'.*

Expert viewpoint 1: This higher-level response describes the effects of Portia's legal arguments upon Shylock. It also makes inferences about the connotations of the language she uses and provides supporting evidence. It discusses the writer's techniques, using literary terms to good effect. The sentences are a little long, but nonetheless ideas are explored very successfully.

Expert viewpoint 2: This mid-level response highlights the effect of what Portia says in the courtroom and how Shylock is affected by this. However, the quotation, though appropriate, is not sufficiently embedded in the sentence. There is one instance of the writer's technique mentioned but no others and in the final sentence the point made is not developed and no evidence or examples are given.

❸ Which comment belongs to which answer? Match the paragraph (A or B) to the expert's feedback (1 or 2).

Student A: .... Student B: ....

❹ Now, take another **aspect** of the scene and on a separate sheet of paper write your own **paragraph**. You could **comment** on one of these aspects:

- The Duke's introduction and Portia's entrance
- The changes of mood throughout the scene
- The end of the scene

Now read this **lower-level** response to the following task:

Read from 'By my troth, Nerissa ...' (I.2.1) to '... worthy of thy praise'. (I.2.110)

Question: *How does Shakespeare introduce Portia, Nerissa and the setting of Belmont in Act I Scene 2? Refer closely to details from the extract to support your answer.*

Student response

> *The first scene including Portia and Nerissa is Act I Scene 2. The scene takes place at Portia's home in Belmont. Portia says: 'By my troth, Nerissa, my little body is aweary of this great world.' This shows that Portia is sad and also that Nerissa and Portia are close friends.*
>
> *Portia says that she cannot choose who she wants to marry and she and Nerissa make fun of all Portia's suitors, except one who is 'a Venetian, a scholar and a solder, that came hither in the company of the Marquis of Montferrat.' This links with Bassanio in Act I Scene 1.*

Expert viewpoint: This answer demonstrates straightforward and sound understanding. The quotations could be shorter and the comments more focused on Shakespeare's language choices and their effects.

5 **Rewrite** these **paragraphs** in your own words, improving them by addressing:

- The lack of development of linking of points – no **'zooming in'** on **key words and phrases**
- The need to use shorter and more embedded quotations
- Limited vocabulary and use of specialist terms

Paragraph 1:

In this scene, Shakespeare presents Portia and Nerissa ... .

....

....

This suggests that ... .

....

....

Paragraph 2:

In a link to the previous scene, ...

....

....

However, Shakespeare contrasts Belmont with Venice by... ....

....

....

This implies that... ....

....

....

6 Write a **full-length response** to this exam-style task on a separate sheet of paper. Answer both parts of the question:

> Question: *How does Shakespeare present the legal system and the theme of justice in* The Merchant of Venice*?*
>
> Write about:
>
> - How Shakespeare presents the workings of the Venetian legal system
> - How Shakespeare presents the theme of justice in general

Remember to do the following:

- Plan **quickly** (no more than 5 minutes) what you intend to write, jotting down **four or five supporting quotations**.
- Refer closely to the **key words** in the question.
- Comment on what the writer does, the **techniques** he uses and the **effect** of those techniques.
- Support your points with **well-chosen quotations** or other evidence.
- Develop your points by **'zooming in'** on particular **words** or **phrases** and explaining their **effect**.
- Be **persuasive** and **convincing** in what you say.
- Carefully check your **spelling**, **punctuation** and **grammar**.

PROGRESS LOG [tick the correct box]   Needs more work ☐   Getting there ☐   Under control ☐

Further questions   (A01) (A02) (A03) (A04)

1 To what extent do you view Shylock as a villain?

2 How does Shakespeare present Portia and Bassanio, both as individuals and as a married couple?

3 What is the dramatic significance of Act III Scene 1 in the context of the rest of the play?

4 To what extent would you say that *The Merchant of Venice* is a play about prejudice?

5 Read from: *'Come on, Nerissa; I have work in hand'* (III.4.57) to *'For we must measure twenty miles today.'* (III.4.84) How does Shakespeare explore the idea of disguise here and elsewhere in the play?

PROGRESS LOG [tick the correct box]   Needs more work ☐   Getting there ☐   Under control ☐

PART TWO: PLOT AND ACTION

Act 1 Scene 1 [pp. 8–9]

1 a) T; b) T; c) F; d) T; e) T; f) F; g) F

2 a) We learn that Antonio is a merchant with many projects and ventures. We also learn that he is sad, and that he has a circle of friends, which includes his particular friend Bassanio.

b) Bassanio seems pleasant, optimistic and charming. We learn that he has amassed debts and that he is coming to Antonio as a close friend to ask for financial help.

c) Bassanio tells Antonio that Portia is a beautiful, wealthy and virtuous woman who lives in Belmont. He describes how she has been left a fortune, and that many suitors are going to see if they can win her hand in marriage.

3

Point / detail	Evidence	Effect or explanation
1: Shakespeare presents Gratiano as concerned about his friend Antonio.	'You look not well, Signor Antonio.' 'Believe me, you are marvellously chang'd.'	Gratiano's comments show he is sensitive to this dramatic change in his friend.
2: Gratiano suggests that some people stay quiet to seem wise but in actual fact they don't have anything interesting or wise to say.	'a wilful stillness' 'dress'd in an opinion' 'I do know of these / That therefore only are reputed wise / For saying nothing'	Gratiano describes how some people cultivate an illusion of being wise. He uses images of a stagnant pond and of clothing to convey the idea that it is just a superficial appearance, and not true wisdom.
3: He is thought of as a funny character who talks a lot of nonsense.	'Gratiano speaks an infinite deal of nothing' 'His reasons are as two grains of wheat …'	His friends seem to suggest that he is entertaining but that there is little substance to what he says.

Act 1 Scene 2 [pp. 10–11]

1 a) The Neapolitan prince; b) England; c) Monsieur Le Bon; d) The County Palatine; e) The Prince of Morocco

2 a) Portia says that she is world-weary and is frustrated that she is not able to choose or refuse potential husbands for herself. Her heart and her head pull her in different directions.

b) Portia's father said that the man she marries must pass a test by choosing the right casket from a choice of three, one of gold, one of silver and one of lead.

c) Portia and Nerissa seem at ease in each other's company. They speak in prose, which helps to establish a sense of closeness and genuine friendship even though they are also mistress and maid.

3

Point / detail	Evidence	Effect or explanation
1: Portia is relieved that her suitors are leaving Belmont.	'there is not one among them but I dote on his very absence.'	The word 'dote' shows how much she longs for them to go. 'Dote' describes fond feelings towards a person, so the idea of doting on someone's absence is oxymoronic.
2: She does not wish to become Morocco's wife.	'I had rather he should shrive me than wive me.'	She says that even if Morocco is a very virtuous man, he would make a better priest than a husband.
3: She remembers Bassanio with enthusiasm.	'Yes, yes, it was Bassanio! – as I think so was he called.' 'I remember him worthy of thy praise.'	Portia seems to be much more animated when speaking about Bassanio compared to her other suitors. She agrees with Nerissa's positive words about him.

Act 1 Scene 3 [pp. 12–13]

1 a) 4; b) 2; c) 5; d) 1; e) 7; f) 3; g) 6

2 a) Shylock lends to Bassanio because Antonio agrees to a form of insurance called a bond if the loan is not repaid. The bond is that Shylock would be able to take a pound of flesh from anywhere he chooses on Antonio's body.

b) Shylock describes Antonio criticising him openly for charging interest on his loans. Antonio has spat on him, called him names and accused him of being a 'misbeliever' (someone who has false beliefs).

c) Bassanio initially seems comfortable with the arrangement that is being negotiated and asks Shylock to dine with them. He thinks at first Shylock is offering kind and friendly terms but grows wary when Shylock names his 'forfeit'.

3

Point / detail	Evidence	Effect or explanation
1: Shylock criticises the way Antonio lends money without charging interest.	'He lends out money gratis, and brings down / The rate of usance here with us in Venice.'	He shows Antonio's negative impact on the living he and others can make as professional moneylenders through enjambment, which emphasises the word 'down'.
2: He says that Antonio criticises Jews in general and him personally and professionally.	'He hates our sacred nation, and he rails / Even there where merchants most do congregate /On me, my bargains, and my well-worn thrift /Which he calls interest.'	Shylock describes how Antonio has publicly humiliated him by personally attacking him, the Jewish faith and moneylenders in the most public of places.
3: He uses strong words to describe his intense feelings of dislike towards Antonio and his desire for revenge.	'I hate him for he is a Christian' 'Curs'd be my tribe / If I forgive him!'	In this aside, the word 'hate' indicates the strength of Shylock's feelings. His language shows how motivated he is and that he thinks revenge rather than forgiveness is the only course of action that can be justified.

Act II Scenes 1 and 2 [pp. 14–15]

1 a) T; b) T; c) F; d) F; e) T; f) F; g) T

2 a) Lancelot debates whether he should go or stay in a comic soliloquy at the start of the scene. He decides in the end to run away and leave his master.

b) Lancelot's father Old Gobbo is blind and easily confused. We learn that Margery is Gobbo's wife and Lancelot's mother.

c) Bassanio offers Lancelot employment. Lancelot is delighted to accept and get away from Shylock.

3

Point / detail	Evidence	Effect or explanation
1: *Old Gobbo does not recognise his son.*	*'Do you not know me, father?'*	*Lancelot plays tricks on his father, taking advantage of his blindness and confusion. This could also be seen to pre-echo Shylock not knowing Jessica.*
2: *Shakespeare creates opportunities for visual humour.*	*'Thou hast got more hair on thy chin than Dobbin my fill-horse has on his tail.'*	*At this point, Old Gobbo thinks he is holding on to a long beard when he is actually clutching Lancelot's hair.*
3: *The two men mispronounce various words and sayings.*	*'His father, though I say't, is an honest, exceeding poor man and, God be thanked, well to live.'*	*In one of many comic confusions in the scene, Gobbo contradicts himself here saying that he is both 'exceeding poor' and 'well to live' (well-to-do).*

Act II Scenes 3 to 6 [pp. 16–17]

1 Lancelot says goodbye to Shylock's daughter **Jessica** as he leaves to work for **Bassanio**. She gives him a **letter** which he passes to **Lorenzo**. They secretly plan for Jessica to leave her home dressed in **male** clothing and taking with her some of Shylock's **gold / money / ducats** and **jewels**. Even though he does not wish to attend the feast, **Shylock** likes the idea of wasting Bassanio's **money**. He instructs Jessica to stay at home but she elopes with Lorenzo, pretending to be his **torchbearer** as they prepare to enjoy the masque with their friends.

2 a) Jessica describes her life at home as 'hell'. She complains about the 'tediousness' of life there without 'merry' Lancelot for company, and sees her relationship with Lorenzo as a means of escape.

b) Lorenzo thinks Jessica is beautiful and he calls her 'fair' and 'gentle'. He cares for her ('never dare misfortune cross her foot'), and calls her his 'love' and 'sweet' once they are together.

c) In Act II, Gratiano is preparing to accompany Bassanio to Belmont, and is also a 'masquer' enjoying the company of friends in Venice, including Lorenzo. In Scene 6 he reflects on human nature, describing the contrast between anticipation and fulfilment: 'All things that are / Are with more spirit chased than enjoy'd.'

3

Point / detail	Evidence	Effect or explanation
1: *Shylock thinks Lancelot is lazy and greedy.*	*'Snail-slow in profit, and he sleeps by day / More than the wildcat. Drones hive not with me'*	*Shakespeare uses a series of animal images to convey Lancelot's laziness.*
2: *He takes a dim view of the partygoers.*	*'Let not the sound of shallow foppery enter / My sober house.'*	*The word 'foppery' shows us that Shylock views this behaviour as frivolous, and warns his daughter to be on her guard against it.*
3: *He wants both Bassanio and Antonio to suffer.*	*'I part with him, and part with him / To one that I would have him help to waste / His borrow'd purse.'*	*Shylock wants Bassanio to spend his money wastefully and hopes to damage the fortunes of both Bassanio and Antonio – with fatal consequences for the latter.*

Act II Scene 7 [pp. 18–19]

1 a) Gold, silver and lead; b) Nine; c) desire; d) A skull; e) A rhyme written on a scroll

2 a) Morocco presents Portia as a perfect idealised woman: 'all the world desires her'; 'this mortal breathing saint'. He praises her beauty several times.

b) When Morocco reads the inscription on the silver casket, he questions whether he deserves someone of Portia's beauty and stature, before deciding that he does. He dismisses the lead as too 'base' and 'gross' and chooses gold because it matches Portia: 'Never so rich a gem / Was set in worse than gold'.

c) Morocco's final words imply that he is devastated by his loss. He uses oppositions to convey his extreme disappointment, from 'heat' to 'cold' and 'frost'. Portia's appears very relieved: 'A gentle riddance!'

3

Point / detail	Evidence	Effect or explanation
1: *The inscription is written in short rhyming lines, with one end-rhyming sound throughout.*	*'Often have you heard that told. / Many a man his life hath sold / But my outside to behold.'*	*The short lines and use of rhyme create a playful tone, rather like a riddle.*
2: *The short poem addresses the failed suitor directly.*	*'Had you been as wise as bold, / Young in limbs, in judgement old, / Your answer had not been inscroll'd.'*	*The use of 'you' and 'your' makes the inscription's message very direct. The tone mocks and teases the reader, listing their faults and reminding them of their failure.*
3: *Shakespeare creates some stark contrasts.*	*'Gilded tombs do worms infold.'* *'your suit is cold'*	*Shakespeare uses oppositions to highlight and emphasise the complete contrast between winning and losing.*

ANSWERS

Act II Scene 8 [pp. 20–21]

1 a) 2; b) 5; c) 3; d) 4; e) 1

2 a) Solanio and Salarino are sharing gossip and hearsay. Their conversation reports what has happened or may have happened off-stage and gives us a sense of the views and attitudes of Venetian society more generally.

b) Their language towards Shylock is insulting as they call him 'villain Jew' and 'dog Jew'. They mock his reaction to Jessica's disappearance, and describe how 'all the boys in Venice' also mock him.

c) It is clear that Salarino and Solanio are very loyal and supportive of Antonio even when he is not there in person. Salarino comments on his great kindness and reports what Antonio said to Bassanio and the manner in which he said it, emphasising Antonio's devotion to his friend.

3

Point / detail	Evidence	Effect or explanation
1: Solanio and Salarino say Shylock was behaving strangely.	'a passion so confus'd, / So strange, outrageous, and so variable'	They use many adjectives to emphasise Shylock's confusion and repeat 'so' three times for effect.
2: The losses of Shylock's daughter and his money are presented as equally devastating losses.	'"My daughter! O my ducats! O my daughter!"'	These exclamations imply that Shylock is muddled and heartless. The way the men report Shylock's reaction makes him seem ridiculous.
3: Solanio and Salarino mock Shylock's reaction to his losses.	'Why, all the boys in Venice follow him, / Crying his stones, his daughter, and his ducats.'	They show that he has become a much-mocked figure on the streets of Venice.

Act II Scene 9 [pp. 22–3]

1 a) T; b) F; c) T; d) T; e) F; f) F

2 a) He says that the oath he has taken means that he is sworn to secrecy about which casket he chooses, that he must never again ask a woman to be his wife, and that he must leave immediately if he fails.

b) He doesn't choose gold because he does not find the idea of what 'many men desire' appealing and, in a superior tone, refers to 'the fool multitude that choose by show'. He believes he is deserving of Portia so chooses silver.

c) Both Nerissa and Portia are eager to see the new arrival. The phrases 'Cupid's post' and 'Lord Love' convey their excitement that such an attractive suitor has arrived.

3

Point / detail	Evidence	Effect or explanation
1: Shakespeare uses the simile of a swallow that builds a home outside rather than inside to criticise Morocco's choice.	'Which pries not to th'interior, but like the martlet / Builds in the weather on the outward wall,'	Arragon is saying that he doesn't just rely on outward appearances, which means he doesn't make the same mistake as Morocco.
2: Shakespeare gives Portia a metaphor to compare the behaviour of her suitors to moths.	'Thus hath the candle singed the moth.'	She compares her failed suitors to moths because they are harmed by the thing that attracted them.
3: Shakespeare uses the words of the messenger to compare the 'young Venetian' and Bassanio to spring and summer.	'A day in April never came so sweet / To show how costly summer was at hand / As this forespurrer comes before his lord.'	The image of spring turning into summer gives an impression of abundant riches to come. This shows how eagerly anticipated Bassanio's arrival is – and suggests that his servant has also made a favourable impression in his own right.

Act III Scene 1 [pp. 24–25]

1 a) 4; b) 2; c) 6; d) 3; e) 1; f) 5

2 a) The rumour persists that Antonio has lost a ship in a dangerous stretch of water. At the end of the scene, Tubal reports that Antonio's financial situation has suffered and that bankruptcy seems inevitable for him.

b) Tubal says he could not find her but spoke to people who had seen her in Genoa. He says that Jessica has been spending her father's money – 'four score ducats' (eighty ducats) in one night – and bought a monkey with a precious turquoise ring that had been her mother's.

c) Shylock is extremely upset by the reports of his daughter's spending. This is alleviated to some extent by the 'good news' of Antonio's misfortunes, which he seems impatient to hear about from Tubal: 'What, what, what? Ill luck, ill luck?'

3

Point / detail	Evidence	Effect or explanation
1: Shylock suggests that Antonio is going to get what he deserves.	'Let him look to his bond. He was wont to call me usurer; let him look to his bond.'	Shylock repeats the phrase 'let him look to his bond' showing that he is determined to exact his revenge.
2: Shylock argues that taking revenge on someone who has wronged you is a natural human reaction.	'And if you wrong us, shall we not revenge? If we are like you in the rest, we will resemble you in that.'	Shylock's use of a rhetorical question makes revenge seem a natural and logical course of action.
3: He suggests that in having his revenge, he will only be copying what Antonio has taught him.	'The villainy you teach me I will execute, and it shall go hard but I will better the instruction.'	Rather menacingly, Shylock says he will be such a good student of Antonio's that he will improve on what he has been taught (implying his revenge will be even greater).

Act III Scene 2 [pp. 26–7]

1 a) She does not want him to choose the wrong casket; b) An instrument of torture; c) Music plays; d) Lead; e) Gratiano

2 a) Salerio bring a letter which says that all of Antonio's ventures have failed and all his ships are wrecked. Salerio also reports that Shylock cannot be swayed and is determined to have his revenge on Antonio.

b) Portia describes the immediate and devastating effect of the news on Bassanio and the physical change she sees in him as a result. Another effect is that Bassanio speaks to Portia seriously and openly about Antonio's problem and his own part in causing it, a change in tone from earlier in the scene.

c) Portia's response is practical and helpful: she is prepared to use her fortune to help Antonio and restore peace and contentment to Bassanio's 'unquiet soul'. She also remains positive and attempts to keep the mood merry and celebratory.

3

Point / detail	Evidence	Effect or explanation
1: The mood is at first romantic and celebratory.	'Good joy, my lord and lady!'	Portia and Bassanio are congratulated by Nerissa and Gratiano.
2: The letter changes Bassanio's mood and he speaks to Portia honestly about Antonio and the bond.	'Here are a few of the unpleasant'st words / That ever blotted paper.' 'When I told you / My state was nothing, I should then have told you / That I was worse than nothing.'	Shakespeare contrasts Bassanio's elation with his despondence by having Portia remark on the suddenness of his change in mood. Bassanio believes that this is the worst news he could have received. The financial and emotional loss is so great that he feels reduced to 'nothing' by it.
3: Portia lifts the mood with her practical help and support.	'You shall have gold / To pay the petty debt twenty times over.'	Portia is resourceful and attempts to keep the mood cheerful. The adjective 'petty' shows that she may at this point underestimate the gravity of the situation.

Act III Scenes 3, 4 and 5 [pp. 28–9]

1 a) 3; b) 4; c) 2; d) 7; e) 6; f) 1; g) 5

2 a) Shylock grows more confident that he will be successful in claiming his pound of flesh and his revenge against Antonio. He speaks abruptly to both Antonio and his jailer and reprimands the 'naughty' jailer for taking any notice of Antonio's requests.

b) Portia says that she knows it is the right thing to do and that she will not regret 'doing good'. She adds that helping people she loves and the people who are most dear to them is really the same as helping herself.

c) We learn that Balthazar is to deliver a letter to Portia's cousin in Padua and to return with 'notes and garments'. Although she has said they will go to a monastery two miles away, Portia and Nerissa are also making plans to travel 'twenty miles today' but Portia does not share all of the details.

3

Point / detail	Evidence	Effect or explanation
1: Portia teases Nerissa about her plan.	'they shall think we are accomplished / With that we lack'	Shakespeare uses humour to show that Portia has a quick-witted and rebellious side to her character.
2: Lancelot Gobbo – now in Bassanio's employment – fondly teases Jessica.	'Therefore be o'good cheer, for truly I think you are damned.'	Through Lancelot's teasing of Jessica, Shakespeare adds pathos.
3: Lorenzo pokes fun at Lancelot and his choice of words.	'The fool hath planted in his memory / An army of good words'	Shakespeare uses humour to dispel tension and create contrasts.

Act IV Scene 1 [pp. 30–1]

1 a) F; b) T; c) F; d) F; e) F; f) T; g) T

2 a) The Duke of Venice is the highest authority in the city: he oversees the smooth running of the trial with the help of his court officers, and acts as a judge to give a verdict on the case. Portia addresses him as 'your grace' and presents her legal arguments to him.

b) Portia shows great skill in her handling of the trial: she speaks and behaves as a lawyer, fooling everyone with her disguise. She wins Shylock's support by upholding the legality of his bond but then undermines his claim for a pound of Antonio's flesh by insisting that he must take exactly the right amount of flesh and must spill no blood.

c) Portia asks Bassanio for his ring to put his loyalty to the test, as he had sworn in Act III that he would never remove the ring. The women want to prove the point that their husbands should be constant in their affections but they do not keep up the deception for long, and harmony is restored once they have taught their husbands a lesson.

3

Point / detail	Evidence	Effect or explanation
1: Characters on both sides trade insults with each other.	'this currish Jew' 'Would any of the stock of Barrabas / Had been her husband, rather than a Christian!'	Shakespeare creates a confrontation where there is hatred and distrust between the two sides in this dispute.
2: Tension mounts when Portia says the bond is lawful.	'there is no power in Venice / Can alter a decree established'	Portia makes it clear that Shylock is entitled to take his pound of flesh. Her words empower Shylock, and he flatters the young lawyer.
3: Shakespeare raises the tension even further when Shylock prepares to take his 'pound of flesh'.	'And you must cut this flesh from off his breast; / The law allows it, and the court awards it.'	The directness of Portia's diction – and the assonant vowels in 'flesh' and 'breast' – draw attention to the extremely violent act that is about to take place.

Act IV Scene 2 and Act V Scene 1 [pp. 32–3]

1 *With the help of **Gratiano**, Portia and Nerissa (still in disguise) arrange for Shylock to sign the deed passing his wealth to **Jessica**. They plan to leave Venice and reach **Belmont** a day before their husbands. Gratiano brings with him Bassanio's **ring** and Nerissa says in an aside that she will see if she can get Gratiano to make the same gesture as Bassanio. Back in Belmont, Lorenzo and Jessica speak in the **garden** and listen to **music**. Portia and Nerissa return, followed by **Antonio**, Bassanio and Gratiano. The husbands struggle to explain why they gave away their rings to **Balthazar** and his **clerk**. Eventually Portia explains everything and the happy ending is complete when Nerissa gives Lorenzo the deed, and Antonio says that his **ships** have returned safely.*

2 a) The storyline involving the rings and the discussion between Lorenzo and Jessica in the garden both tackle the issue (first raised by Gratiano in Act II Scene 6) of what happens after the excitement of winning someone's heart is over and married life begins.

   b) For all of the reasons mentioned above, there is much that is happy and celebratory at the end of the play. But modern audiences might feel that Shylock's fall casts a shadow over the jubilant mood and may feel pity for his plight.

   c) The atmosphere at the end of Act IV Scene 1 remains tense and the remaining scenes lighten the mood and return the characters to the pleasant setting of Belmont. These scenes also resolve Shakespeare's final plot twist regarding the rings.

3

Point / detail	Evidence	Effect or explanation
1: When Nerissa gives Lorenzo Shylock's deed, Shakespeare resolves the future of Lorenzo and Jessica.	'My clerk hath some good comforts too for you'	The word 'comforts' brings warm reassurance to Lorenzo and Jessica who were facing an uncertain future.
2: We hear that Antonio's ships are safe.	'three of your argosies / Are richly come to harbour suddenly.'	After all the rumours and worries, this news provides assurance that Antonio is out of trouble.
3: Shylock does not appear in the final two scenes and is barely mentioned.	'There do I give to you and Jessica / From the rich Jew, a special deed of gift / After his death of all he dies possess'd of.'	This is the final mention of Shylock in the play and it concerns his wealth rather than the man himself.

PART THREE: CHARACTERS

Who's who? [p. 35]

1 Top row, left to right: Venetian merchant; Portia; Venetian lord, suitor to Portia

   Middle row: Shylock; Portia's lady-in-waiting; gentleman, marries Nerissa

   Bottom row: Lorenzo; servant to Shylock and later Bassanio; Shylock's daughter, marries Lorenzo

2

Royalty / nobles	Venetian citizens	Venetian Jews	Servants, messengers, etc.
Duke of Venice	Solanio	Tubal	Old Gobbo
	Salarino		Stephano
Prince of Morocco			Leonardo
			Salerio
Prince of Arragon			Balthazar

Antonio [p. 36]

1

Antonio's business dealings as a merchant	1 He is a successful merchant with business ventures all over the world.
	2 He doesn't charge interest on loans.
Antonio's attitude towards Shylock	1 He has treated Shylock with disrespect and prejudice in the past.
	2 He accepts the terms of Shylock's loan and seems resigned to the consequences.
Antonio's friendship with Bassanio	1 He has great affection for Bassanio and seems to care for little else.
	2 He lends to Bassanio very freely.

2 a) Antonio: 'In sooth I know now why I am so **sad**' (I.1.1)

   b) Gratiano: 'You have too much **respect** upon the world.' (I.1.74)

   c) Salarino: 'A **kinder** gentleman treads not the earth.' (II.9.36)

   d) Shylock: 'Jailer, look to him. Tell not me of mercy. / This is the **fool** that lent out money gratis.' (III.3.1–2)

   e) 'I am a **tainted** wether of the flock' (IV.1.114)

Portia [p. 37]

1 a) F; b) T; c) T; d) F; e) T; f) NEE

2 a) Portia shows a cruel side to her character when *she makes mocking remarks about her suitors, particularly about Morocco's 'complexion'.*

   b) When Bassanio is successful in the casket test, Portia reacts by *speaking very humbly about herself and giving him a precious ring that Bassanio must never 'part from, lose, or give away'.*

   c) Portia's performance as a lawyer in the trial scene is *skilful and ultimately successful. She shows mastery of legal language, rhetoric and questioning.*

   d) We learn that Portia enjoys having power over other characters in the play, when *she plans her elaborate strategy to help Antonio, and when she asks Bassanio for his ring and then accuses him of giving it away.*

Shylock [p. 38]

1 *Shylock is a Jewish usurer or **moneylender** living in Venice. In Act I Scene 3, he agrees to the loan of three thousand **ducats** as an act of friendship, saying he will forget **Antonio**'s harsh treatment of him in the past. However, the bond they agree allows Shylock to claim a pound of the merchant's **flesh** if the money is not repaid within **three** months. In Act II, Shylock's **daughter** Jessica runs away with Lorenzo, taking many of her father's **valuables** with her. In Act IV Scene 1, **Portia**'s legal skills deprive Shylock of his revenge. Ultimately Shylock is not treated mercifully by the **Christian** establishment. In the final two scenes, Shylock does not **appear** at all.*

2, 3 There is no one correct set of answers here.

Bassanio [p. 39]

1 a) Portia; b) Shylock; c) Nerissa; d) Portia

2 a) Bassanio asks Antonio for money because he has run up debts – and not for the first time. He now needs money in order to be able to go to Belmont to woo Portia and asks Antonio because his patron has been generous to him in the past.

b) Bassanio is positive about his meeting with Shylock at first. However he becomes wary of Shylock by the end of Act I Scene 3 urging his friend, 'You shall not seal to such a bond for me'.

c) Bassanio courts Portia with gifts, but when he hears the worrying news about Antonio in Act III Scene 2, he is much more open with her about his financial situation and his guilt because he has allowed Antonio to take great risks for his sake. Later, the incident with the rings again calls his loyalty to Portia into question, but all is happily resolved by the end of the play.

Other characters [pp. 40–1]

1 a) Nerissa; b) Lancelot Gobbo; c) Duke of Venice; d) Gratiano

2 a) I think Lancelot Gobbo is significant to the play as a whole because *he is an entertaining comic figure, and his movement from Venice to Belmont helps to bring the two worlds of the play together.*

b) I think Lorenzo is significant to the play as a whole because *his love for Jessica is a trigger for her elopement and Shylock's despair and desire for revenge.*

c) I think Salarino and Solanio are significant to the play as a whole because *they represent the views of Venetians more generally, and they frequently report action that has happened off-stage.*

3

	Gold casket	Silver casket	Lead casket
Inscription	'Who chooseth me, shall gain what many men desire.'	'Who chooseth me, shall get as much as he deserves.'	'Who chooseth me, must give and hazard all he hath.'
Contents	Death's head (skull)	Picture of a fool	Picture of Portia
Who chose it?	Morocco	Arragon	Bassanio

4 What do you think each suitor's choice of casket suggests about his character?

Prince of Morocco: his pride and boastfulness
Prince of Arragon: his sense of his own superiority over the 'multitude'
Bassanio: his ability to see beyond appearances

5 There is no one correct set of answers here.

PART FOUR: THEMES, CONTEXTS AND SETTING
Themes [pp. 43–6]

1 Likely answers: mercy, love, risk, revenge, chance, family, the law, money, appearance versus reality, prejudice, justice and injustice, marriage

Possible answers: violence, greed, conflict, power

Less likely answers: ambition, guilt, beauty, evil, fate

2 a) Theme(s): family, marriage — Speaker: Portia
b) Theme(s): appearance versus reality — Speaker: Morocco
c) Theme(s): revenge — Speaker: Shylock
d) Theme(s): mercy, the law — Speaker: Portia
e) Theme(s): prejudice — Speaker: Shylock
f) Theme(s): money — Speaker: Shylock

3 a) *Bassanio's debts; the loan and the risks of not repaying; Jessica leaving with Shylock's riches, and her spending; Shylock not receiving his forfeit in the form of money (or flesh); the loss of Shylock's wealth*

b) *Portia's successful suitor would claim a dowry as well as her hand in marriage, so love and money, marriage and inheritance are closely connected. Portia tries to use her money to help Antonio but in the end she must make a different kind of intervention to save the day.*

4 Test 1: the casket test

Themes: marriage, appearance versus reality, chance

Test 2: the courtroom scene

Themes: the law, justice and injustice, mercy, revenge

Test 3: the giving of the rings

Themes: love, marriage, loyalty

5 Portia and Nerissa:

- They are mistress and servant but they also seem to be good friends. They confide in each other and joke wittily. Their use of prose shows that they enjoy each other's company and can speak informally and entertainingly with each other, gossiping about Portia's suitors, or coming up with secret plans.

Antonio, Bassanio and Portia:

- Antonio seems more private and more prone to melancholy but his affection for his young friend Bassanio is sincere and motivates Antonio's decision-making in the play. Portia's devotion to Bassanio is also very strong and so she treats Antonio as she would her own husband, knowing that to help Antonio out of difficulty is to come to Bassanio's aid too.

6

Reveals these attitudes	Describes being the victim of such attitudes
Gratiano: 'infidel'	Shylock: 'You call me misbeliever, cut-throat dog, / And spit upon my Jewish gaberdine.'
Antonio: 'I am as like to call thee so again, / To spit on thee again, to spurn thee too.'	Shylock: 'He hath … cooled my friends, heated mine enemies – and what's his reason? I am a Jew.'
Portia: 'Let all of his complexion choose me so.'	Morocco: 'Mislike me not for my complexion'

7 a) mercy, *e.g. key theme of Portia's courtroom speech; Antonio's support for Bassanio despite his profligate ways in the past*

b) vengeful, *e.g. Shylock's plans to take revenge on Antonio; Jessica spending her father's money in Genoa; the way Shylock is treated after the trial?*

c) There is no one correct answer for this question.

8

Point / detail	Evidence	Effect or explanation
1: Shakespeare presents the union of Bassanio and Portia as a moment of sheer joy and elation.	'Giddy in spirit' (Bassanio) 'Happiest of all' (Portia) 'you have bereft me of all words' (Bassanio)	Adjectives like 'giddy' and 'happiest' show that true affection has a deep impact on characters.
2: Shakespeare reveals a different side to marriage through the other suitors Portia encounters.	'I can bid the other four farewell'	Portia happily bids her other suitors farewell – her father's test means that she has little control over who she marries.
3: Shakespeare uses this scene to show the harmony that marriage brings as Gratiano and Nerissa announce their love too.	'I do beseech you / Even at that time I may be married too.'	In many Shakespearean comedies, more than one marriage is announced, creating a mood of alliance and harmony.

Contexts [pp. 47–8]

1 a) 1590s; b) *Il Pecorone*; c) Christopher Marlowe; d) The ghetto; e) The Queen's doctor; f) He was executed; g) Non-Jewish; h) Dowry

2 a) There are several insulting remarks made about Shylock because of his race and religion. It is only Shylock who voices criticism of this treatment, suggesting that anti-Semitic attitudes were commonplace and that stereotypical portrayals of Jewish characters were not offensive to Shakespeare's audiences at the time.

b) 'Interest' (or 'usance') is mentioned in the play in relation to Shylock's working practices and is a key point of difference between Antonio who doesn't charge interest and Shylock who does. This is mentioned in several places in the play including Act I Scene 3, Act III Scene 1 and Act III Scene 3.

c) The play opens and closes with scenes in which ships and mentioned, and news of the safe passage or misfortunes of ships have a powerful effect on characters in the play. There are several reminders of the sea and of Venetian canals, for example in Act II Scene 8 which opens with Salarino saying 'Why, man, I saw Bassanio under sail' (line 1) and 'In a gondola were seen together / Lorenzo and his amorous Jessica' (lines 8–9).

3 a) Padua: Where Portia's cousin Doctor Bellario lives. Balthazar travels here to take a letter to Bellario.

b) Venice: One of the play's main settings Major port and centre of trade Antonio is a merchant from this city-state.

c) Genoa: A major Mediterranean port. It is reported that Jessica spends a great deal of Shylock's wealth here.

d) Naples: A prince from this place is one of Portia's failed suitors.

Settings [p. 49]

1

Questions	Venice	Belmont
Is it a real place or a fictitious place?	real	fictitious
Which scenes take place there? Circle the correct scenes.	I.1, I.3 II.2, II.3, II.4, II.5, II.6, II. 8 III.1, III.3 IV.1, IV.2	I.2 II.1, II. 7, II.9 III.2, III.4, III.5 V.1
Which major characters live there?	Shylock, Antonio, Bassanio	Portia
Which key events take place there?	trial scene	casket tests

2 a) Act III Scene 5 takes place in: Portia's garden in Belmont

Who it involves: Lancelot, Jessica, Lorenzo

Why the setting is important: the scenes set in the rural location of Belmont feel distant from the main action in Venice despite the characters and storylines that connect the two places; the garden in particular is a peaceful and restful setting in stark contrast to the busy, bustling streets of Venice

b) Act IV Scene 1 takes place in: courtroom in Venice

Who it involves: Duke, Antonio, Bassanio, Salerio, Gratiano, Portia, Nerissa, and Shylock

Why the setting is important: this long scene takes place in the formal environment of a courtroom, a suitably grand location as the main storyline reaches its climax and the themes of the law and justice and injustice are explored

c) Act IV Scene 2 takes place in: a street in Venice

Who it involves: Portia, Nerissa, Gratiano

Why the setting is important: the action takes place in Venice in the immediate aftermath of the tense trial scene

PART FIVE: FORM, STRUCTURE AND LANGUAGE

Form [p. 51]

1 Five

2 Comedy

3 A play within a play

4 *Enter* Portia *disguised as Doctor Balthazar, followed by officials* (Act IV Scene 1)

Arragon *unlocks the silver casket (Act II Scene 9)*

Enter Lancelot Gobbo, *the Clown, alone (Act II Scene 2)*

Enter Jessica *above, in boy's clothes (Act II Scene 6)*

Venice: a street. Enter Portia *and* Nerissa *(Act IV Scene 2)*

Enter Stephano *with musicians (Act V Scene 1)*

5 There is no one correct answer for this question.

Structure [pp. 52–3]

1 a) F; b) T; c) T; d) F

2 'The quality of mercy is not strain'd' (Portia, Act IV, Scene 1)

'So may the outward shows be least themselves' (Bassanio, Act III Scene 2)

'Let me play the Fool.' (Gratiano, Act I Scene 1)

3 There is no one correct way to complete this task.

4

Point / detail	Evidence	Effect or explanation
1: Shakespeare uses the bond that is agreed to in Act I to foreshadow later events.	'I like not fair terms and a villain's mind.'	Bassanio casts Shylock in the role of 'villain', setting up the dark conflict at the heart of the play.
2: Shakespeare moves the action to Belmont in Act II, and Portia's witty commentary on her suitors.	'PORTIA: When they do choose / They have the wisdom by their wit to lose. NERISSA: The ancient saying is no heresy: / "Hanging and wiving go by destiny."'	The use of rhyming couplets here emphasises the clever wit shared between Portia and Nerissa and keeps the mood light.
3: When the action moves back to Venice, Lancelot Gobbo makes a typically comical appearance to defuse tension.	'I am Lancelot your boy that was, your son that is, your child that shall be.'	Lancelot Gobbo acts the role of the play's fool, breaking the tension and undermining serious themes, for example the importance of family bonds.

Language [p. 54]

1 a) Solanio: 'Nature hath fram'd strange fellows in her time:

Some that will evermore peep through their eyes,

And laugh like **parrots** at a bagpiper'

b) Shylock: 'The patch is kind enough, but a huge feeder,

Snail-slow in profit, and he sleeps by day

More than the wildcat.'

c) Bassanio: 'Thus ornament is but the guiled shore

To a most dangerous **sea**'

d) Gratiano: 'for thy desires

Are **wolfish**, bloody, starv'd and ravenous.'

e) Lorenzo: 'When the sweet wind did gently **kiss** the trees,

And they did make no noise.'

3

a) Flesh and/or blood Act III Scene 1	The idea of flesh and blood relates to the theme of family. As Salarino says to Shylock, 'There is more difference between thy flesh and hers than between jet and ivory; more between your bloods than there is between red wine and Rhenish.' He is saying that even though Shylock and Jessica are family, they are totally different – perhaps because Jessica is marrying a Christian man.
Act IV Scene 1	The motif also relates directly to the bond – 'a pound of flesh' – and to Portia's legal arguments that save Antonio from a painful repayment – and certain death – in this scene.

b) Ships and the sea Act I Scene 1	The play opens with Antonio describing his sadness and Salarino and Solanio attempting to comfort him. Their imagery is of the sea – where merchants' fortunes are won and lost. Salarino tells Antonio that his 'mind is tossing on the ocean' and develops this in a powerful extended metaphor.
Act II Scene 8	The motif recurs whenever characters refer to the whereabouts and possible misfortunes suffered by Antonio's merchant ships.
c) Chance or risk Act I Scene 1	Bassanio uses the image of an archer shooting an arrow in the same direction as the first. He argues that 'by adventuring both/I oft found both'. He admits this is a rather naïve 'childhood proof' but encourages his patron to take a risk on him.
Act II Scene 7	This motif runs through the casket test scenes, for example when Morocco exclaims 'Hazard for lead!' in response to the inscription: 'Who chooseth me, must give and hazard all he hath.'

3

Point / detail	Evidence	Effect or explanation
1: Shylock is spoken about using anti-Semitic insults.	'thou damn'd inexecrable dog' 'Thou almost mak'st me waver in my faith, … That souls of animals infuse themselves / Into the trunks of men.'	Gratiano compares Shylock to animals. He is saying he is barely human and that he will not receive God's grace. This shows the intensity of his antipathy and prejudice.
2: Shakespeare's characters also show their intense feelings of love and affection.	'From the corners of the earth they come / To kiss this shrine, this mortal breathing saint.' '… yet for you / I would be trebled twenty times myself, / A thousand times more fair …'	Much of the language of courtship and love in the play uses superlatives, hyperbole and classical allusions to praise the object of affection.
3: Shylock seems to confuse his grief at the loss of his daughter with his grief at the loss of his money.	'Justice! The law! My ducats and my daughter!'	The exclamations signal both his confusion but also the intensity of his reaction to his losses.

PART SIX: PROGRESS BOOSTER

Writing skills [pp. 58–9]

2 Student A: Mid

Clear point that provides evidence in the form of a quotation. Explanation needs to be more developed.

Student B: Higher

Clear and perceptive point. Effective choice of quotation and focus on what that quotation implies. Further explanation develops main point further.

3 The phrase 'chief care' shows that Bassanio's debts are a matter of great concern to him.

ANSWERS

4, 5 and 6

*In this scene **Shakespeare** shows us that Portia is quick-witted when she is talking with her friend and lady-in-waiting Nerissa. Portia **states** that she 'dote[s] on [their] very absence' when she is talking about her suitors. She is **implying** that she will be glad when they have left Belmont. It not only **demonstrates** that she is becoming impatient with all her unsuitable suitors but it also **signals** that she is independent.*

Making inferences and interpretations [p. 60]

1 Simple point: first sentence; develops: second sentence; inference: third sentence

2 c)

Writing about context [p. 61]

1 b)

2 a)

Structure and linking of paragraphs [pp. 62–3]

1 Topic sentence: *Shakespeare presents Venice as a centre of business and trade.*

Quotation word: *'credit'*

Explains: *relates to the fact that Antonio has 'Neither … money nor commodity' to offer Bassanio so must resort to borrowing money instead.*

2 Possible answer:

Shakespeare presents Portia as a character who is both practical and playful. Portia says to Nerissa that she has a plan but that she won't tell her everything until they are in the carriage. She teases her and keeps her guessing, saying it's 'work in hand / That you know not of'. By referring directly to Nerissa's lack of knowledge about the plan and by drawing attention to her teasing manner with alliteration ('know not of'), Portia is manipulating Nerissa into wanting to 'know' more.

3 Topic sentence: *We see a more antagonistic side to Gratiano when he speaks to Shylock in the trial scene.*

Change: *His appearance in this scene contrasts greatly with earlier scenes*

Links: *when, implying, a view which he, in the scenes where*

Spelling, punctuation and grammar [p. 64–5]

3 *In the first scene, Shakespeare **firmly** establishes the **friendship** between two major **characters**, Antonio and Bassanio. The **audience** also learns about the **wealthy** Portia and the younger man's plans to woo her. Antonio agrees to help Bassanio who is **grateful** to his patron. However, Antonio cannot raise the money without a **loan**, and so they agree to see a moneylender.*

4 *Shakespeare **sets** his play in **Venice. At** the time this was a major centre of **trade. The** play's title makes many references to **trade. The** professions of the 'merchant' of the title **(A**ntonio) and Shylock are extremely important to the plot **as, when** Antonio says, 'I'll seal to such a **bond,'** he is agreeing to something that will put his life in **danger**.*

5 Student B

6 *In a comic soliloquy in Act II Scene 2, Lancelot Gobbo <u>debates</u> whether to leave 'this Jew my master' or to stay. His language in this speech <u>borrows</u> from the morality play tradition; his 'conscience' and a 'fiend' <u>speak</u> to him in two different voices. Shakespeare <u>gives</u> Lancelot long words and long sentences and <u>makes</u> him stumble over them: 'and, in my conscience, my conscience is but a kind of hard conscience.' The playwright <u>contrasts</u> the grand and ambitious style of the clown's language and the humorous effects it <u>creates</u> for the audience to enjoy.*

Tackling exam tasks [pp. 66–7]

1 <u>How</u> does <u>Shakespeare</u> <u>explore</u> the <u>different kinds of bonds </u>that <u>connect people</u> in *The Merchant of Venice*?

Write about:

- Ideas about <u>relationships</u> between family members, friends, etc.
- The <u>techniques</u> <u>Shakespeare</u> uses to <u>explore</u> these ideas

Sample answers [pp. 68–71]

1 Student A: Expert viewpoint 1; Student B: Expert viewpoint 2

2 Student A: Expert viewpoint 2; Student B: Expert viewpoint 1